A JEWEL IN THE CROWN

A JEWEL IN THE CROWN

A
History
of
Crystal Growth Research
at
RRE/RSRE, Malvern, UK

Donald T. J. Hurle
and Keith G. Barraclough

A Jewel in the Crown:
A History of Crystal Growth Research at RRE/RSRE, Malvern, UK
Donald T. J. Hurle
and Keith G. Barraclough

Published by Aspect Design 2014
Malvern, Worcestershire, United Kingdom.

Designed, printed and bound by Aspect Design
89 Newtown Road, Malvern, Worcs. WR14 1PD
United Kingdom
Tel: 01684 561567
E-mail: allan@aspect-design.net
Website: www.aspect-design.net

ISBN 978-1-908832-66-5

Behind almost every electronic
device lies a single crystal.

W. G. Pfann

CONTENTS

LIST OF PHOTOGRAPHS

FOREWORD

At the end of the Second World War Field Marshal Montgomery wrote to the then Director of the Research Establishment at Malvern to express his gratitude for the crucial contribution it had made to the successful outcome of the recent conflict through its contributions to radar technology. After the war research continued at Malvern through a period that was to see a revolution in electronics technology and the increasing tension of the Cold War.

Fundamental to the electronics revolution was the new field of solid state electronics and optics. An increasing number of new devices were being invented, each crucial to the collection and management of the information so important in any conflict but each in turn dependent upon the provision of new electronic materials. Whilst there were many electronic disciplines that contributed to the maintenance of a national technological edge, a foundational discipline was inevitably the preparation and characterisation of the necessary materials. As the stresses of the Cold War increased, maintenance of that technological edge became ever more important, and in a sense that war was, in part, fought out in the laboratories of Malvern.

This account of crystal growth is one of many remarkable stories of technical achievements made at Malvern in the post-war years. What is often overlooked is the contribution made by the work to wider society. Out of this work on electronic materials, for example, have come improvements in the field of medicine, such as various forms of body scanners and thermal imagers. In the home new communication capabilities have benefited from work originally motivated by a perceived defence need.

Why was research at Malvern so fruitful? Some years ago a study at Harvard Business School concluded that the ideal environment for innovation is one in which a clear understanding of current needs is brought alongside technical excellence. This, I believe, was the secret of the success of the Establishment: military staff, with their expert knowledge of the limitations of current weapon systems, worked with very bright scientists who had a deep knowledge of their subject and the ability and opportunity to think laterally.

As one who in his time benefited from the work of the materials scientists in provision of samples for my own work, it is a pleasure to express my gratitude and commend this history of the many achievements of the crystal growth scientists at Malvern. It would be gratifying if the publication of this book could be followed by similar books covering other areas of research within the Establishment. As a later Director of the Establishment, I would like to commend this book to a variety of readers:

• Those who wondered what people did behind that fence for so many hours each day. In this book they will get a glimpse of the remarkable achievements made here in the laboratories.

• Those who delight in ownership of the many powerful electronic devices available today. They will glimpse here something of the problems that had to be solved and were largely solved at Malvern, to make these products possible.

• Those who would like to learn lessons on the management of innovative technology. They will find some salutary lessons here.

Dr Chris Baynham,
Director RSRE, 1984–1986

PREFACE

After the end of the Second World War many government defence establishments remained in existence to ensure that UK capability continued to be state of the art, since defence systems depend heavily on a wide range of technologies. Following the invention of the transistor in 1947, the period of the Cold War was a golden age for the development of Solid State Electronic technologies that were to become of pivotal importance to defence capabilities.

Research and development in electronics, optics and related technologies was spearheaded at the Telecommunications Research Establishment (TRE), Malvern, later known as the Radar Research Establishment (RRE), the Royal Radar Establishment, (RRE) and the Royal Signals and Radar Establishment (RSRE).

Whilst the wartime radar work of TRE has been well documented, the post-war era of RRE/RSRE has little recorded history. We have attempted to rectify that for one area within the Establishment's Physics Group: the Division concerned with the growth, characterisation and provision of single crystals of materials required for making new types of solid state devices. The Division not only pioneered the growth of crystals of a large number of new materials, but also developed new techniques for crystal growth which became used in industry worldwide. It became internationally recognised as a leader in the field and played a significant role in establishing crystal growth as a discipline in its own right.

Proud to have been members of that Division, our aim has been to produce an accurate account and evaluation of the crystal growth research carried out until $c.$1990, when the status of the Establishment changed to that of an executive agency of the Ministry of Defence. Although some materials research continued at Malvern until $c.$2010, the Electronic Materials Division ceased to exist after 1991. We have attempted to describe the science and technology in terms that can be understood by an interested layperson. However, complex technical terms are sometimes unavoidable and so a simple glossary of these has been added for expressions labelled with a^G. The book is not, and could not be, a detailed account of everything and of everyone involved. It is hoped that it will provide a valuable archive to some future historian who undertakes to write a wider history of the work of the Establishment.

We have done our best to check the veracity of all that is in the book but, inevitably, there will be some omissions and mistakes, for which we apologise.

Donald T. J. Hurle, Keith G. Barraclough

ACKNOWLEDGEMENTS

It would not have been possible to write the book at all without the help of many former colleagues, too numerous to mention individually, who provided technical information, anecdotes and photographs. We are extremely grateful to them all. The project benefited from the encouragement of Dr Chris Baynham, and we are grateful to him for writing the foreword.

We thank our respective wives, Pamela Hurle and Jane Barraclough, for their support throughout the year that it has taken us to prepare the manuscript. We also thank Hugh Williams of the Malvern Radar and Technology History Society, MRATHS, for his help and support in providing links to the past.

We gratefully acknowledge all copyright holders of photographs indicated at the end of each caption. Special thanks are due to QinetiQ plc, the current custodian of the original Crown Copyright images. Finally, we thank all the staff of Aspect Design for their skills and cooperation in transforming our raw manuscript into the published article.

I
THE EVOLUTION OF
THE MALVERN ESTABLISHMENT

In May 1942 the Telecommunications Research Establishment (TRE) with more than half of its two thousand workers, including all of its scientific staff, was hurriedly moved—'before the next full moon' as instructed by the Prime Minister, Winston Churchill—from its location near to Swanage at Worth Matravers on the Isle of Purbeck. It came to Malvern College, a boys' public school in Worcestershire, the boys having been swiftly re-accommodated at Harrow public school. This action was taken because of fears that the Nazis were planning to raid the Worth Matravers site. At about the same time the Air Defence Research and Development Establishment (ADRDE) at Christchurch, also on the south coast, was moved to Pale Manor in North Malvern, later to be renamed the Radar Research and Development Establishment, (RRDE). The vital role played by both establishments in the war effort is quite well known. The work of TRE during the war years has been documented by its Director, Dr A. P. (Jimmy) Rowe.[1]

With the end of the war in 1945 came the question of what to do with the two establishments. The crucial role that science and technology had played in determining the outcome of the war pointed to the need for Britain to maintain a state of the art capability in radar and other newly emerging technologies. An exhausted Rowe retired

---

[1] A. P. Rowe, *One Story of Radar* (Cambridge University Press, 1948).

Visit of HM Queen Elizabeth II and HRH the Duke of Edinburgh to South Site in 1957, accompanied by W. J. Richards, Director. In the background, top right, is K-building under construction. Copyright © QinetiQ plc.

as Director of TRE in 1945, to be replaced by his deputy, Wilfrid B. Lewis. In c.1947 TRE moved from the Malvern College site to a former Royal Navy training establishment, HMS *Duke*, on St Andrews Road (South Site). A recent book by Ernest Putley traces the Establishment's work on radar up to 1953, the year in which TRE and RRDE were amalgamated into a single establishment and renamed the Radar Research Establishment (RRE).[2] In 1957 HM Queen Elizabeth and HRH the Duke of Edinburgh visited the Establishment, going first to the Pale Manor site (North Site) and then to South Site where Her Majesty honoured the Establishment by renaming it the Royal Radar Establishment, thus retaining the letters RRE. Since that time, it has been shuffled between government departments, finally being given

[2] Ernest Putley *Science Comes to Malvern. TRE. A Story of Radar, 1942–1953* (Aspect Design, Malvern, 2009).

the name Royal Signals and Radar Establishment (RSRE) by HM the Queen when she and HRH the Duke of Edinburgh again visited the Establishment in 1976. RSRE became part of the Defence Research Agency, DRA, in 1991 and the Defence Evaluation and Research Agency, DERA, in 1995 before becoming part of a government owned plc known as QinetiQ which was floated on the London Stock Exchange in 2006.

2
THE FORMATION OF A PHYSICS GROUP

Ernest Putley wrote that Lewis sought to transform the Malvern sites into a National Electronics Research Establishment but was unable to do so. He did, however, manage to put in place a Physics Group as part of TRE, headed by Robert A. Smith (affectionately known as 'RA'). In 1946, almost a year after becoming TRE Director, Wilfrid Lewis left to take up a post with the Canadian Atomic Energy Authority at Chalk River.

Physics Group was housed in the old wartime buildings on South Site until 1958 when a new purpose built laboratory (designated K-Building) was opened on the site by the Right Honourable Aubrey Jones MP, the last Minister of Supply.

The invention of the transistor[G] in December 1947 by Bardeen, Brattain and Shockley at Bell Laboratories, New Jersey, USA was the birth of the solid state era. This breakthrough heralded an upsurge of worldwide interest in germanium and silicon semiconductors[G] used to make this new device, and there followed the discovery of a steadily increasing number of new materials and devices with useful and novel functions. Clearly, the preparation and properties of these materials would need to form part of the ongoing programme of the new TRE Physics Group.

This book charts how that research programme evolved from small beginnings over nearly four decades into a core enabling technology: *crystal growth.* Crystal growth is the key element in materials

The newly occupied K-Building *c.*1958, with the wartime F-Block in the foreground. P4 subsequently occupied the top floor. Copyright © QinetiQ plc.

technology that has made possible not only the development of components for military systems; it has also enabled the production of a whole range of consumer products—computers, smart phones, TVs, satellite navigation and so much more—that are changing the world at a rate not known by previous generations.

What are crystals?

A simple description of a ***crystal*** is a material in which the atoms (or molecules) are located at the intersections of a three dimensional lattice which can be repeated over large distances, giving the structure long range order. Notable examples in this context are the semiconductors, silicon and germanium. Some materials such as glass have a disordered structure and are primarily non crystalline at normal temperatures. All crystals are ordered structures but, depending on the nature and degree of order, there are different types as outlined below.

A ***polycrystal*** (in special cases also referred to as a ***multicrystal***) is one in which the material contains numerous tiny crystal grains having a different orientation from their neighbours, with irregular boundaries between them known as grain boundaries. In a **single crystal** there are no grain boundaries, so the spatial periodicity of the lattice is maintained throughout the whole crystal specimen without any change in orientation, perhaps over tens of centimetres. A **liquid crystal** is something entirely different. It is, as the name implies, a certain type of fluid that can flow and spontaneously form an ordered **crystal-like** structure by the application of an electric field.

The properties of a **solid crystal** are very dependent on imperfections, known as defects, in the lattice. Major defects such as grain boundaries in a **polycrystal** are extremely harmful to the electronic and optical properties of semiconductors. In this book, we are largely concerned with the preparation of **single crystals** and improvements in their structural perfection down to the atomic level for electronic and optical applications. However, grain boundaries in **polycrystals** and the structure of certain glasses impart useful properties such as mechanical hardness to many solids. We shall also be concerned with some aspects of **polycrystals** and glassy materials, particularly for those applications in which sensitive electronic devices need to be protected from harsh environments, such as airborne sensors on fast jet aircraft.

Liquid crystals are the basis of modern displays in mobile phones, computers and televisions. The Physics Group of RSRE played a major role in the development of **liquid crystal** technology but this is a separate subject beyond the scope of the present book. We are concerned solely with the preparation and characterisation of materials in the solid state.

Crystal growth

In the context of electronic and optical devices, single crystals are usually required in one of two forms: bulk crystals and epitaxial layers. Bulk crystals may be in the form of a solid state laser rod, for example, or a semiconductor substrate[G] formed by slicing up a bulk sample into wafers. Such bulk crystals are commonly 'grown' by carefully solidifying a melt, slowly cooling a solution of the substance in a solvent or condensing a vapour. The other crystal form is an epitaxial layer, where the word 'epitaxial' implies that a layer grown onto a crystalline substrate replicates the periodic structure of the substrate lattice. Epitaxy can be of two types: homo-epitaxy in which the substance being grown is a thin layer of the same material as the substrate; and hetero-epitaxy in which the layer is grown on to a foreign substrate but nevertheless grows as a single crystal with an orientation determined by that of the substrate. A wide variety of techniques has been developed to produce such layers.

Interest in the form and growth of natural crystals dates back centuries but a detailed understanding of how crystals grow did not come until the twentieth century. The discovery of X-ray diffraction[G] by W. L. Bragg in 1913 made possible the determination of crystal structures. By the end of the 1940s, there was a good understanding of how crystal nuclei were formed, and there were models of how a three-dimensional nucleus grew by the formation of two dimensional nuclei on its faceted surfaces. The nuclei could expand laterally by accreting atoms from the liquid or vapour at the step formed by such a nucleus on the surface.

Theoretically, the rate of growth of a crystal by this mechanism is determined by the rate at which these two-dimensional nuclei are formed and this, in turn, is related to the supersaturation[G] of the phase from which it is growing. However, the theories predicted a rate of growth that was many orders of magnitude smaller than that observed! This discrepancy was explained when, in 1949 at a now famous meeting of the Faraday Society in Bristol, F. Charles Frank, a Bristol University physicist, showed that if a lattice defect, now known as a screw dislocation[G], intersected the growing surface it would provide a source of surface steps that would perpetuate growth even at very low supersaturation. At that same meeting Joe Griffin, of Royal Holloway College, produced the first pictures of such a dislocation on a crystal surface.

All this knowledge was to prove very valuable later when epitaxial growth became important (chapter ten). However, it was of little use to a study of the growth of most crystals from the melt because, in general,

F. Charles Frank (later Sir Charles)
delivering a lecture on dislocations.
Copyright © Ian Saunders.

the growing surface of the crystal is atomically rough at the melting point and atoms can be accreted at all points on it without any need for steps or two dimensional nuclei. Under these conditions the rate of growth is controlled, not by the formation of nuclei, but by the rate at which the heat liberated by crystallisation is taken away. It soon became evident that the way in which this happens can have a profound effect on the perfection of the crystal. When the melt contains more than one component, then crystallisation produces a solid of a composition that, in general, differs from that of the melt. This segregation of components at the growing crystal-melt interface produces concentration gradients in the melt that can give rise to instability of the growth surface with consequent defect formation. The Faraday Society Meeting in 1949 contained nothing of this; what little was known at that time was in the metallurgical field. The RRE/RSRE materials group acquired an international reputation for its pioneering work in this subject and for devising means for eliminating these and other defects.

Infrared detectors

The earth's atmosphere permits transmission of invisible infrared radiation (heat) in two important wavebands: the 3–5 micron[G] and the 8–14 micron wavebands. The 3–5 micron band permits detection and imaging of very hot objects such as aircraft and rocket engines by certain types of semiconductor[G]. Similarly, objects at temperatures close to room temperature can be detected in the 8–14 micron band— for example, thermal images[G] of heat loss from domestic buildings.

Towards the end of the war in Europe the Allies captured a German infrared detector which used galena—the natural ore of lead sulphide

(PbS)—that was able to detect hot targets. Making and studying PbS semiconductor detectors became the first project of the newly formed TRE Physics Group. In 1948, on the initiative of George MacFarlane, attempts were made to grow single crystals of the other semiconducting lead chalcogenides[G], and in 1951 Bill Lawson reported on the growth of single crystals of lead telluride (PbTe) and lead selenide (PbSe), achieved by lowering a charge of the material contained in a silica ampoule through a heated zone. Detectors made from the PbTe crystals were fitted to a Firestreak infrared homing missile in 1953/54. Ernest Putley continued research to improve these detectors. Their limitation was that their performance did not extend out to the 8–14 micron ('room temperature') band and so, for night vision applications, new materials had to be found.

In c.1957 Bill Lawson, Stan Nielsen and Alex Young conceived the semiconductor that today is the universally used material for infrared detection in the 8–14 micron atmospheric transmission window when the highest performance is required. That material is a mixture of cadmium telluride and mercury telluride (CMT). The operational waveband of a semiconductor detector is determined by a property known as its band gap.[G] Mercury telluride has too small a band gap whilst cadmium telluride has too large a one. Since the two materials have the same crystal structure, it was reasoned that, by forming a mixture of the two, the band gap could be tuned to the desired value. This prediction proved to be correct and the preparation and properties of CMT were reported by Bill Lawson, Stan Nielsen, Ernest Putley and Alex Young in 1959. However, the technical problems of growing such crystals were formidable and were not satisfactorily solved until decades later. The fiftieth anniversary of the demonstration of a CMT detector at Malvern was celebrated at a meeting in Orlando, Florida in 2009 when Tom Elliott was the principal speaker.

Before the discovery of CMT and its applicability to the 8–14 micron atmospheric window, a new material for use in the 3–5 micron window was identified in Germany. As the military interest at the time was only in detecting hot objects such as jet engines, work on this

Bill Lawson (centre), Stan Nielsen (right) and Alex Young (left), discoverers, in 1957, of cadmium mercury telluride as an infrared detector material. Copyright © QinetiQ plc

new material was given priority over the CMT work. (Bill Lawson managed to preserve UK work on CMT with a contract at Mullard, Southampton).

Two newly recruited post-doctoral researchers set out to grow single crystals of the new material, the semiconducting compound indium antimonide (InSb). Brian Mullin was a chemist who had studied the presence of gold in sea water at Liverpool University and Ken Hulme, a physicist who had studied the growth and structure of zinc single crystals at Bristol University under Professor F. Charles Frank. They purified the synthesised InSb by zone refining^G—a method discovered earlier by W. (Bill) Pfann at the famous Bell Laboratories in New Jersey, USA—to extremely high levels of purity. The purification process was studied using radioactive 'tracer'^{G} elements, with support from Olly Jones, a radiation chemist, recruited from the nuclear reactor site at Windscale. Using this material they grew single crystals by pulling from a melt. Ernest Putley designed and fabricated infrared detectors using these crystals.

Schematic representation of the elements of crystal pulling from a melt. Heating of the melt is shown to be by radio frequency (r.f.) power.

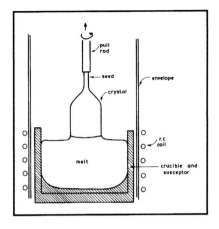

The crystal pulling method, credited to J. Czochralski, a Polish scientist, had been developed by Gordon Teal and John Little at Bell Laboratories to produce the semiconductor, germanium. This was a pioneering piece of work. Prior to it, the controlled growth of single crystals by pulling was virtually unknown. (Czochralski had pulled wires of low temperature metals from a melt-containing crucible for the purpose of studying the maximum speed of crystallisation of each metal). Nowadays it is the preferred method for producing bulk single crystals of a very wide range of materials on an industrial scale.

In essence the method consists of a heater and crucible in which the charge to be melted is placed. Mounted co-axially above the crucible is a pulling rod onto the lower end of which is affixed a chuck that holds a small piece of single crystal (the 'seed'). Motors attached to the pull rod enable it to be raised and lowered smoothly at very low rates (down to less than one millimetre per hour) whilst being slowly rotated. The whole, except for the motors, is enclosed in an air-tight chamber that can be evacuated or filled with an inert gas such as argon at atmospheric or high pressure. Following melting of the charge, the seed crystal is slowly lowered until it touches the melt surface and the melt temperature is adjusted until the seed crystal supports a small column of melt (a meniscus). When the system is stabilised thermally, the pull rod is raised slowly, resulting in crystallisation on the end of the seed. The diameter of the crystal can be increased or decreased by tiny adjustments to the heater power. The process is shown schematically in the line diagram.

In the course of their work Ken Hulme and Brian Mullin made an important fundamental discovery. They found that when a crystal of InSb was grown from a melt with the temperature distribution in the growth chamber, such that the crystallising surface was convex toward the melt, facets formed on parts of the growing surface. These facets delineated the closest packed planes of the atoms in the crystal. When very small amounts of certain elements (called dopants[G]) were added to the melt, these facets incorporated the dopant preferentially, resulting in a spatially non-uniform distribution of the dopant in the crystal. They named this 'the facet effect'. It has subsequently been found to be a general phenomenon in those classes of material that form such facets. The knowledge of this has been important in understanding and controlling the chemical uniformity of a wide range of crystals having commercial application.

Germanium and silicon

About the same time as Ken and Brian were working on indium antimonide a programme to study the semiconducting materials germanium and silicon was started. A junior lecturer from Royal Holloway College, William (Bill) Bardsley was recruited to the Transistor Physics Division in c.1952 to produce single crystals of germanium and silicon. Bill worked with an Experimental Officer, Geoff Green, and together they designed a versatile high precision machine for pulling crystals from the melt (Czochralski growth). Initially, the pullers were made in the excellent workshops on the Establishment. With this machine, Bill and Geoff produced state of the art single crystals of germanium and silicon. Using these crystals, Alan Gibson and colleagues were able to make fundamental studies of them and to fabricate and investigate the properties of devices made from them, notably the transistor[G].

Bill and Geoff went on to design a floating zone refiner[G] to purify polycrystalline silicon rods and to convert them into single

Left: the original Bardsley-Green crystal puller on display at the 'Challenge of the Chip' exhibition at the Science Museum, London, 1980. Right: an early photograph (*c.*1958) of a silicon crystal being pulled from the melt.

crystals. The acquisition of these technologies was vital to the Group's attempt to catch up with the work in the USA in organisations such as Bell Laboratories, IBM, Texas Instruments and Westinghouse. The robustness of the floating zone refiner was demonstrated by Geoff when he took the equipment to the Institute of Physics Annual Exhibition held in the Royal Horticultural Society Halls in London, *c.*1961. Despite the floor vibration and temperature fluctuations, he successfully grew a single crystal rod of silicon on each of the two days of the exhibition, an achievement that attracted much interest and praise. It nearly did not happen. A mobile crane was needed to lift the heavy equipment from a lorry to place it on the top of the steps leading into the building. Police arrived and refused to allow this to be done. However, a diversion was arranged to attract their attention and the task was quickly completed!

At the end of 1959 Don Hurle was recruited as a Junior Research Fellow (JRF), a three-year appointment. He came following completion

Some Transistor Physics Group staff celebrating Jo Callan's twenty-first birthday in the Railway Inn, Malvern in 1957. From left to right, front row: Barrie Straughan, Shirley Murray, Jean Hutcheon, Geoff Green, Jo Callan, Bill Bardsley; back row: Patrick Hoyland, unknown, John Morgan, unknown, Chris Baynham, unknown, unknown, Alan Gibson, Ron Bell, unknown. Copyright © QinetiQ plc

of a PhD at Southampton University for which he studied the growth and high temperature electrical properties of bismuth single crystals. He was placed with Bill Bardsley's section in the Transistor Physics Division which at that time was endeavouring to grow single crystals of germanium, very heavily doped with either gallium or arsenic. The crystals were to be used to fabricate tunnel diodes[G], newly invented by Leo Esaki in Japan.

The problem was that, as the concentration of the dopant in the crystal was increased, a point was reached where its distribution became highly non-uniform on a microscopic scale and with very high densities of dislocations[G]. Finally, polycrystallinity occurred, with the formation of large numbers of defects known as 'twins'. By good fortune, Don had studied similar behaviour during the growth of bismuth single crystals and he identified the problem as being due to a phenomenon given the name constitutional supercooling[G] which had very recently been discovered in metals by a group led by Professor Bruce Chalmers at Toronto University. Don extended the theory of the effect to the case where the melt was being stirred by the rotating crystal and, with Bill Bardsley and Jo Callan, revealed in detail the mechanisms by which the dopant non-uniformity and high dislocation density occurred. Valuable information was obtained by Andrew Lang and Michael Hart at Bristol University using X-ray diffraction topography[G] (a technique invented by Andrew) to image dislocations. Finally, Don was able to define experimental conditions that yielded uniformly doped, low dislocation density crystals (grown by Hugh Chedzey) having the desired dopant concentration for the fabrication of tunnel diodes.

3
AN ELECTRONIC
MATERIALS DIVISION IS FORMED

The pioneering work on the crystal growth of lead chalcogenides, germanium, silicon, indium antimonide and CMT in the 1950s had been carried out in three small divisions within Physics Group, each with its own head. However, it soon became apparent from the difficulties of preparing compound semiconductors that more focus should be given to the basic materials science and the subject of crystal growth in particular. By c.1961 the Division, named Semiconductor Materials and Devices and led by Bill Bardsley, had subsumed the materials research on indium antimonide within the Infrared Devices Division, including Brian Mullin, Ken Hulme and some support staff. Around this time it was also decided to cease work on CMT, with the result that Bill Lawson's Division on Solid State Materials dispersed. By November 1962, Stan Nielsen and some support staff from Bill Lawson's Division had joined Bill Bardsley's new Electronic Materials Division which now had a total of twenty-three staff. Initially designated PC Division within Physics Group, it eventually became known as P4 Division.

Bill Bardsley remained in charge as Superintendent for nearly twenty years. The Division expanded steadily in the following decades as more and more materials became of importance to the Establishment. The following was Bill's vision as stated in an internal booklet entitled, 'The RRE Electronic Materials Division':

At this point it is pertinent to define the objectives of the Division, the areas of innovation and the facilities needed to achieve these.

Solid state science and technology in the service of military and civil needs demands a steadily increasing range of ever more closely characterised and perfect materials. The successful development of many solid state devices depends on the availability of well characterised high quality single crystals of the essential materials. Other components call for polycrystalline and glassy materials which need to be explored.

The successful prosecution of this branch of materials research calls for innovation in four main areas:

1. The discovery and development of new materials and the improvement of existing ones.

2. The progressive development of the equipment and technology of crystal growth in order to make possible the fabrication of single crystals of materials, hitherto considered to be too difficult.

3. The scientific understanding of those fundamental aspects of crystal growth which bear upon the control of crystal properties and perfection.

4. The exploitation of new techniques for the characterisation of these materials.

Crystals for solid state lasers

Interest in new materials of potential importance to meet military requirements soon widened beyond the semiconductors. In 1960 the invention of the solid state laser by Ted Maiman at Hughes Laboratories in the USA led to research world-wide into the growth of a wide range of potentially suitable crystals (mainly high melting point refractory oxides) variously doped, mostly with rare earth elements[G]. The Establishment's initial interest in such lasers was for optical range finding and Geoff Green initiated work in this field by growing doped calcium fluoride single crystals. In 1962 Brian Cockayne, a metallurgist from Birmingham University, was recruited to lead the work. The versatile RRE-developed crystal puller proved ideal. Brian and Martin

Chesswas were soon growing single crystals of calcium tungstate, calcium aluminate, yttrium aluminium garnet, yttrium gadolinium garnet, sapphire and ruby. For efficient laser action to take place in such crystals, they had to be of high chemical and structural perfection and controllably doped. Later that year Danny Robertson, a chemist who had been a de Broglie Scholar at the Institut Radium Curie in Paris, was recruited to augment the laser materials work which he did by developing chemical etchants that revealed any defects in the crystals.

The first challenge was to melt the material in a precious metal (platinum or iridium) crucible at temperatures that, for some materials, were very close to the melting points of the crucibles. Inevitably, on the odd occasion, some of these very expensive crucibles were accidentally melted. Brian's measured response to this was always: 'I would rather you had not done that, mate.' Secondly, the defects formed in the crystals had to be understood and means for eliminating, or at least minimising, them devised. To this end the earlier work of Brian Mullin and Ken Hulme on the facet effect proved valuable, as this phenomenon was also found to occur during oxide crystal growth from the melt. Further, constitutional supercooling^G can occur during melt or solution growth of all multi-component materials including oxides. The defects introduced into the crystal by this effect had already been studied in heavily doped germanium by Bill Bardsley and Don Hurle and in indium antimonide by Brian and Don. Comparison of the defects formed in these three classes of material proved to be very valuable. To these phenomena was added the problem of the very large thermal stresses experienced by the crystals as they cooled from their very high growth temperatures, typically around 2,000°C. Means for reducing thermal stress by pulling the crystal into an after-heater assembly that reduced the temperature gradients experienced by the cooling crystal were devised by Brian Cockayne, John Plant and Brian Lent. In the USA researchers in this field mostly came initially from the ceramics field where crystal growth technology was not so advanced as in the semiconductor field. The sophisticated RRE puller gave Brian Cockayne the ability to achieve more control over crystal perfection than most other workers and he rapidly became internationally recognised as a leader in the field.

Brian established links with his alma mater, the Physical Metallurgy and Materials Science Department at the University of Birmingham, which provided additional technical expertise and a source of new recruits. In 1967 Tony Vere was recruited from this department as a Junior Research Fellow to investigate the high temperature mechanical properties of complex oxides, with the aim of understanding the role of defect generation during crystal growth. In c.1968, Brian established a long standing contract with Rex Harris's group in Birmingham to undertake constitutional studies of these complex materials, notably their phase diagrams and solid state phase transformations. Future recruits from Birmingham, Keith Barraclough (chapter nine) and Graham Brown (chapter six), were both introduced to electronic materials as post-doctoral researchers on this contract. Stuart Irvine (chapter ten) was also one of Rex Harris's PhD students.

Later, in the mid 1970s, there was a requirement for lasers operating at a wavelength that was (relatively) eye-safe. Published research had shown that the most promising material for the purpose was lithium yttrium fluoride doped with holmium, together with several other rare earth elements. [G] Crystal growth of this material posed several problems. Firstly, all the elements needed to be purified by zone melting of their fluorides under very dry conditions. The concentrations of the rare earth elements had to be systematically adjusted in a search for the highest laser performance. Brian Cockayne found that very slow growth rates were necessary and crystal defects had to be studied and minimised. Structural characterisation using X-ray techniques (chapter six) was performed in-house by Gordon Jones and Ken Lloyd; extramural support was provided by the contract with Rex Harris and Stuart Abell at Birmingham University.

Crystals for other applications

The demand for new crystals soon expanded beyond semiconductors and laser materials. Around the world, other materials having desirable properties that could be exploited to produce novel devices for a wide range of applications were being crystallised, and requests for P4 Division to produce some of these came in steadily.

In the late 1960s the invention at Bell Laboratories of the magnetic bubble memory[G] stimulated interest worldwide. The device required strain-free single crystal substrates of gadolinium gallium garnet (known as '3Gs'). Brian Cockayne and John Roslington grew such crystals and, with Tony Vere, discovered the mechanisms that could introduce strain in them. Further, they were able to establish growth conditions that avoided this strain. Major advances in silicon memory chips and in computer hard drives soon outstripped the performance of magnetic bubble memories[G] and interest in this technology waned. However, the understanding obtained by Tony and Brian of the mechanisms of strain formation proved valuable in later work.

The very high light intensities that could be obtained from lasers had led to the discovery of new effects in crystals having certain types of crystal structure. These effects, known as non-linear optic effects, included second harmonic generation (frequency doubling). Thus, for example, a neodymium-doped yttrium aluminium garnet laser produces 'light' in the infrared, not visible to the human eye. When shone onto a particular type of non-linear optic crystal, such as barium sodium niobate, that light is converted to the visible green region of the spectrum.

Other devices convert optical signals to electrical ones or electrical to optical ones. Yet others convert temperature changes to electrical signals (pyro-electricity) or pressure changes to electrical ones or vice versa (piezo-electricity). A common use for the latter effect is the igniter on a domestic gas hob where pressing on the piezo-electric crystal produces a spark. Used in more sophisticated ways, crystals exhibiting these effects were being developed for use in signal processing, especially in the radar and communications fields.

Danny Robertson took up this challenge and, using a variety of growth techniques, produced crystals of many different materials at the request of colleagues in other divisions of Physics Group.

His most notable achievement was the production of single crystals of zinc tungstate for use as an X-ray scintillator[G] material in X-ray tomographic[G] brain and body scanners. Use of this material markedly improved the performance of the scanner without increasing the X-ray dose to the patient. An internal report on the work of P4 Division in 1975 lists seventy-nine different materials that had been grown in the Division up to that date. Danny and his assistants, Peter Born, Mike Houlton and Harry Parfitt, were responsible for the production of at least half of these. Growing crystals of new materials is never a routine procedure; each material brings its own problems. Included in Danny's list are nine candidate materials for piezo-electric devices, two for pyro-electric devices (for relatively low cost heat-seeking detectors operating at room temperature, such as those used eventually by the emergency services), two for electro-optic applications, eleven for a variety of non-linear optic applications and two for X-ray tomography.[G]

In 1971 Gordon Jones, a chemist educated at the University of Birmingham, joined the Division from Bell Telephone Laboratories, New Jersey, USA. Initially, Gordon worked with Danny Robertson on the growth of lithium niobate. Later, he worked on the growth and characterisation of lead germanate crystals and, in association with Tony Vere and Norman Shaw, investigated the potential of this material for pyroelectric infrared detectors. Gordon also worked on problems with triglycine sulphate (TGS), as used in pyroelectric devices being made on an extramural contract at Mullard, Southampton for the Chieftain Main Battle Tank; he also worked on the pyroelectric vidicon[G] programme in association with Rex Watton and others from the infrared group.

Technology for the growth of highly dissociable semiconductor crystals

Indium antimonide, studied by Ken Hulme and Brian Mullin, is one of a class of semiconducting compounds having a metal from Group III of the Periodic Table, aluminium (Al), gallium (Ga), indium (In) combined with a Group V element, nitrogen (N), phosphorus (P), arsenic (As), antimony (Sb): the III-V compounds. Growing crystals of the arsenides and phosphides of gallium and indium poses problems not experienced in the growth of germanium (Ge) and silicon (Si), namely dissociation of the material when heated. The Group V element evaporates preferentially compared with the Group III component. For example, if one tries to grow a crystal of gallium arsenide (GaAs) by the conventional crystal pulling method the As in the melt evaporates preferentially and condenses on the cold wall of the chamber leaving a melt which is nearly pure Ga.

Brian had noted a paper from workers at Westinghouse in the USA in which they reported the use of a layer of molten boric oxide floated on the melt of lead telluride to prevent the evaporation of lead telluride molecules. He realised that the same approach should work also for dissociable compounds even though evaporation rates could be very much higher. He carefully applied the technique first to

Brian Mullin explaining the fundamentals of high pressure LEC crystal growth.
Copyright © Don Hurle

GaAs and found that conditions could be obtained whereby the boric oxide wetted the surface of the growing crystal as it emerged from the molten boric oxide encapsulant, thus preventing the dissociation of the crystal as it cooled to room temperature. Furthermore, he found that, by using certain crucible materials, the boric oxide could be made to wet the crucible wall so that the melt and crystal were totally enclosed by boric oxide. Appropriately, Brian named the technique the Liquid Encapsulation Czochralski (LEC) technique. With support from Barrie Straughan, he first used it to grow high resistivity crystals of GaAs needed by another team within the Physics Group to attempt to make field effect transistors[G] for use as microwave amplifiers and digital integrated circuits.[G]

Brian went further. In the case of GaAs the required pressure in the chamber to prevent dissociation was a mere two atmospheres. For indium phosphide (InP), a material then being researched to make high frequency microwave devices, that pressure was twenty-eight atmospheres. That necessitated the development of a pressure chamber for the puller that could both withstand pressures of a few times that for safe operation and be inert to the corrosive phosphorus vapour. Brian designed and had built such a puller in a form that could be incorporated as a drop-in fitment to the standard Bardsley-Green puller. The equipment was licensed to Metals Research of Melbourn in Hertfordshire (a company later to be bought out by Cambridge Instruments) who marketed it worldwide as the 'Malvern' high pressure Czochralski crystal growth system. Brian, Barrie and Anne Royle carried out a pioneering study of the electrical behaviour of a wide range of dopants in indium phosphide grown by the technique.

Independently, Sidney Bass, assisted by Peter Oliver, then at the Services Electronics Research Laboratory (SERL) in Baldock Hertfordshire (chapter seven), built his own LEC pressure puller in which he grew crystals of gallium phosphide (GaP), a material being used to make the early light emitting diode[G] displays for calculators and other instruments. He assisted Metals Research in the use of the 'Malvern' puller to grow GaP single crystals. The technique that he

Brian Mullin's high pressure assembly fitted to a Bardsley-Green puller being used to grow single crystals of indium phosphide by the LEC technique. Inset shows a crystal grown using the automatic diameter control system developed by Gordon Joyce. Copyright © QinetiQ plc

had used to synthesise the GaP polycrystalline charge was later taken up and marketed by Metals Research.

The 'Malvern' high pressure puller became adopted worldwide for GaAs when it was found that it was possible with this puller to obtain, in a single operation, the equi-atomic molten mixture of Ga and As, from which the crystal was to be grown. This was achieved by placing solid As and Ga in the correct proportions into the crucible and placing a disc of boric oxide on top. Then, by very carefully raising the crucible temperature, the Ga could first be melted and would then progressively dissolve the solid As, the boric oxide having already melted and covered both Ga and As. Finally, as the melting point of the compound GaAs was reached (1,240°C), the dissolution of the As was complete. However, to achieve this result, the chamber pressure had to be very much higher than when a pre-fabricated charge of GaAs was used. The merit of this high pressure method, aside from the advantage of being only a single stage process, was that it yielded crystals which had the high electrical resistivity needed to make field effect transistors.[G] Such crystals were said to be semi-insulating (SI). Growing such crystals reliably was difficult with the low pressure process.

Silicon single crystals can be grown entirely free of dislocations, even up to the largest crystal diameters grown commercially (currently 300 mm—chapter nine). Using the high pressure LEC technique, Brian Cockayne and David Hope grew dislocation-free crystals of gallium arsenide of very small diameter, but found that there was a critical diameter (of the order of 1cm) beyond which dislocations were always present.

This new high pressure LEC method for producing crystals of the III-V materials revolutionised the production of GaAs, GaP and InP devices worldwide and made possible the huge market in the ever expanding range of electronic and opto-electronic consumer products we enjoy today.

The LEC technique was not limited to III-V compounds. In the infrared field, the major technical difficulties posed by CMT as a material for detectors in the 8–14 micron waveband led to a continued search for alternative materials. Steve Hiscocks, a metallurgist who had obtained his doctorate of philosophy at Oxford, joined in 1963 and, in collaboration with Tom Elliott in the Infrared Division, started a programme to grow crystals of materials known to have the very small electronic band gaps[G] that could make them contenders. The first studied was platinum antimonide ($PtSb_2$) which was successfully grown by the LEC technique but which proved to have a larger band gap than had been reported in the literature. Solid solutions of lead and tin tellurides (LTT) were more promising and these too were grown by the LEC technique. However, constitutional supercooling[G] and the defects it caused were, as with CMT, very difficult to avoid and required extremely low growth rates. Subsequent advances in CMT technology (chapter ten) meant that this work was not pursued further.

4
THE INTERNATIONAL SCENE

Throughout the 1960s, semiconductor and laser research worldwide was expanding at a tremendous rate, with new devices being invented almost monthly. To keep up with this, attendance and presentation at major international conferences in the field was vital. However, the interests of crystal growers were not well served as crystal growth was not recognised as a discipline in its own right. Crystal growers had to seek acceptance of their papers in conferences where there was no focus on crystal growth, such as those devoted to either physics or chemistry.

The Ministry of Supply sponsored two meetings on electronic materials, limited to the UK. The one at Bangor in 1962 attracted ninety delegates but conference proceedings were not published. When, in 1966, the first truly international conference on crystal growth was held in Boston, Massachusetts, USA, Bill Bardsley, Brian Mullin and Don Hurle attended and presented papers. At that meeting there was a demand that such conferences should be held regularly, with the major contributing countries taking it in turns to host them. This demand was, in part, driven by the discontent of crystal growers in the semiconductor field who felt that the physicists and device engineers got all the credit for advances made, with little or no credit being given to the crystal growers who had made their work possible. Arranging this conference had not been straightforward because crystal growth was viewed differently in different organisations. In the Soviet Union it was seen as a branch of crystallography. In Germany at that time,

Kristallwachstum (the study of the mechanism of crystal growth) was considered an academic subject whereas the production of technically useful crystals (Kristallzüchtung) was held in lower regard.

At an early morning business meeting held during the Boston conference, Bill Bardsley was unanimously elected to chair a provisional committee to organise future conferences. On his return to the UK, Bill quickly arranged with Professor Alan McQuillan of the Physical Metallurgy Department of Birmingham University, the holding of a second International Conference on Crystal Growth at Birmingham University under their joint chairmanship. This conference, given the acronym ICCG2, took place in 1968 and was a great success. (The Boston Conference was retrospectively designated as ICCG1).

Michael Schieber, a young post-doctoral researcher at Harvard University, who had been a driving force in the organisation of ICCG1, foresaw the need for crystal growers to have their own peer-reviewed journal. North Holland Publishing Company (now Elsevier Science) was approached and agreed to publish such a journal under the title Journal of Crystal Growth (JCG). The first edition came out in late 1967 and the Proceedings of ICCG2 (edited by F. Charles Frank, Brian Mullin and Steffen Peiser) was published in JCG. Bill Bardsley and Brian Mullin were amongst its first associate editors. Brian remains an associate editor to this day (2014). In 1980 Don Hurle became a member of the Editorial Board, a position he held for twenty-five years.

ICCG2 brought an enormous benefit to RRE Electronic Materials Division. From its presentations at the conference and from visits to its laboratories after the conference by eminent researchers from across the world, it became recognised as having capability at international level. This opened the door to visits to, and exchange of information with major research laboratories in the USA, continental Europe and Japan. Invitations to make presentations to the prestigious Gordon Research Conferences in the USA were also received and accepted.

At ICCG2, a business meeting appointed Professor Raymond Kern from the University of Marseilles to chair ICCG3 to be held at his University campus in 1971. Associated with this, an International

Summer School on Crystal Growth was held in Nordwijk in the Netherlands during the week prior to the Marseilles conference. At the conference the Constitution for an International Organisation for Crystal Growth (IOCG) was submitted and approved. Bill Bardsley retired as Chair of the interim committee established at Boston in 1966 and F. Charles Frank was elected as the first President of IOCG.

Another outcome of ICCG2 was the formation of the British Association for Crystal Growth (BACG) in 1969 with Alan McQuillan as its first Chairman. Bill Bardsley and Brian Mullin were founding members of its committee. BACG remains, in 2014, a thriving organisation bringing together all the UK crystal growth activity, holding local, national, European and international meetings. A history, celebrating the first forty years, was published in 2009. During that period six RRE/RSRE Materials staff members or ex-members served as BACG Chairman: Bill Bardsley, Brian Cockayne, Keith Barraclough, Don Hurle, Stuart Irvine and Tony Vere. Bill Bardsley and Don Hurle also became Honorary President during their retirement.

BACG, along with more than twenty other national organisations formed following the birth of IOCG, are now affiliated to it. BACG was one of the first of these. Several Electronic Materials Division members have served on the IOCG Council and Brian Cockayne was its Vice President and then President during the period from 1977 to 1992.

Thus, in the short space of five years, crystal growers worldwide came together to form what is now recognised as a discipline in its own right, with national and international organisations holding regular conferences under its auspices, awarding prizes and having international journals devoted to the discipline. Electronic Materials Division staff played a major role in these achievements.

5
A MINISTRY OF TECHNOLOGY INTERLUDE

The Wedgwood Benn vision

During the brief period between 1966 and 1970, when Anthony Wedgwood Benn became Minister of Technology in Harold Wilson's Labour Government, responsibility for RRE was transferred from the Ministry of Aviation to the new Ministry of Technology. This action was part of Wilson's plan to forge a new Britain in the 'white heat of technology'. Benn wanted the government research establishments, including RRE, to do more contract research for industry with some of its scientists and engineers moving from research to work on design, production and marketing of advanced industrial products. In a press release reported in the *Guardian* newspaper in October 1967 Mr Benn is quoted as saying:

> The policy we shall be implementing has not been adopted as a result of undervaluing the importance of research work. It is rather the need to get more qualified people making a contribution to economic advance. [The research establishments contained a] priceless complement of engineers and scientists [and the Government was re-examining their purpose and role.] It would be quite wrong to find work inside Government establishments for its own sake if just to keep scientists and engineers employed. Where possible we shall encourage the establishments to undertake contract research on a basis of

confidentiality to the firm concerned. We shall try to make it easier for people to move between the establishments and industry and bring research, production and marketing closer together. What we are engaged in is not just an attempt to transfer the emphasis from defence to civil work—although we are doing that—but to secure a redistribution of more of our qualified scientists and engineers from research, wherever it is done, into design, development, production, marketing and, above all, management. The integration of research and production has proved to be the secret of industrial success abroad and it must be a major object of policy here.

The notion that staff might be doing work that was found for its own sake would not have been well received!

Describing his department's efforts to spread knowledge about productivity, Mr Benn said that if the standards of the worst firms could be raised to the average level, the increase in productivity would be enough to give Britain growth without inflation and expansion without a trade deficit. 'This would enable us to break out of the cycle of stop and go that has lain like a curse over our economy since the war.' How often that vision has recurred and been dashed since!

In response to all this, RRE produced a document entitled: 'Technical and Research Services for Industry: RRE Activities Guide 1967'. This document contained a list of the functions and facilities of the Electronic Materials Division, P4 and included an appendix describing the newly formed Electronic Materials Information Centre. This centre aimed to provide information to industry and universities on the sources, availability and characterisation of materials of interest to workers in advanced electronics and solid state physics. A second, more detailed booklet entitled 'Mintech: RRE Electronic Materials' describing the wide range of crystals being grown and the techniques used to do so was also produced and widely circulated.

Electronic Materials Unit

A much bigger service to industry and university researchers was conceived and introduced in response to Benn's grand plan. It was to establish an Electronic Materials Unit (EMU) to supply, to academic and commercial customers, crystals and epitaxial layers of electronic materials cut, polished or otherwise prepared to the requirements of the customer. Several staff members were recruited and it commenced operation on a modest scale in May 1967. It was intended that it should receive separate financial support and have separate staff and laboratories nearby but not to be part of RRE. A large steering committee drawn from various organisations was formed to direct its course. However, after a fairly short period of operation with the newly recruited staff working alongside the Electronic Materials Division staff, it was realised that a number of problems would need to be solved before materials could be supplied in reasonable quantity and quality.

Display case in M-Building foyer, showing the wide range of bulk single crystals grown by P4 Division (c.1975). Copyright © QinetiQ plc

In 1970 a new government was elected and Benn's dream died with the disbandment of the Ministry of Technology. The Establishment continued to focus on its defence remit but the EMU remained in a reduced form, incorporated into the Electronic Materials Division as part of the latter's function. It sold, to other UK laboratories in industry and universities, research quantities of those materials that were being grown or had been grown and remained in stock. It fulfilled a valuable function of making available to industry and universities many important new materials that would not otherwise have been available within the UK for early device feasibility and development work. The Unit was managed initially by Steve Hiscocks and, on his departure, by Olly Jones until Olly's retirement in 1981. Cut-backs in the Establishment staffing levels in the 1970s resulted in the originally recruited EMU staff being absorbed within the Division and most of the EMU orders were in fact fulfilled by Division staff. In the decade to 1978 it had completed 1,420 orders comprising some forty different materials (many variously doped and in the form of bulk specimens or epitaxial layers). Materials were charged at the operational cost of producing them and, by 1978, the total value of those orders was £266,000, equivalent to £2.6 million on 2012 prices.

6
A PURPOSE-BUILT MATERIALS LABORATORY

Towards the end of the 1960s, the Division had increased to more than forty staff, with an ever increasing breadth of capability. David Marshall had been recruited from Bell Laboratories, USA, bringing with him expertise on hydro-thermal crystal growth, a technique used for the growth of bulk crystals from a solution at low temperatures and high pressures in cases where normal melt growth techniques cannot be applied (e.g. the growth of quartz crystals). The recruitment of Robin Farrow, a Junior Research Fellow from Queen Mary College, University of London strengthened the capability in epitaxy, especially Molecular Beam Epitaxy (chapter ten). The Division had out-grown its space on the top floor of the Physics Building (K-Building).

K-Building also vibrated when lorries passed in front of it, or when trains passed on the nearby track. This was not conducive to the production of high quality crystals by pulling from the melt—the surface of some melts in the crucible could be seen to have small ripples from the vibrations. Further, the extension of the work of the Division to the growth of epitaxial layers by chemical vapour deposition processes using volatile precursors,[G] some of which were both toxic and pyrophoric, required additional fume extract cabinets and other safety facilities. The Division badly needed a purpose-built laboratory. A request for such a building was made and was granted by Headquarters, thanks much to the efforts of the then RRE Director, (Sir) George MacFarlane.

The new materials building was sited close to its predecessor,

K-Building, by demolishing two pairs of spurs of the wartime F-Block. Designated M-Building, the new building was L-shaped, with the main block of offices and laboratories at right angles to a spur which housed the building's engineering infrastructure and other amenities. Originally, an adjacent building was planned to house the Electronic Materials Unit but this was not funded and the EMU was accommodated within the new building.

Some of the Division's staff were intimately involved in the design of the building and its various facilities. This was masterminded by Geoff Green who brought his considerable experience and expertise to the installation of services in a manner that gave great flexibility and could be carried out by laboratory staff without the need to bring in specialists such as electricians and plumbers. Geoff also designed a central vacuum extract system for cleaning offices and laboratories, especially for removing the toxic dusts that laboratory work might generate. In one of his many detailed memos, Geoff warned M-Building inhabitants to be aware of the vacuum system's powerful suction that was very much greater than that of a domestic vacuum cleaner—personal belongings might be gobbled up and never seen again!

The two floors of air-conditioned laboratories had an area of 16,000 square feet. Above each laboratory, services were readily accessible in a large, six-feet-tall roof void. The bottom and top floors of the three floors of offices, therefore, had ready access via double swing doors to laboratories on the same level. A middle floor of offices was a sort of mezzanine which, according to Geoff, 'formed a kind of peaceful limbo for senior staff.'

Crystal pulling was designed to be carried out in the ground floor laboratories which had two-feet-thick concrete floor slabs not attached directly to the building walls to minimise vibrations. One of the laboratories at ground level also had a floor consisting of a twenty-ton concrete slab floating on servo-controlled pneumatic supports for special experiments. State of the art fume cupboards were a feature of many of the laboratories and could be readily attached to the extract system in the service void.

The main block of M-Building (centre) housed two floors of laboratories (not shown) next to three floors of offices which overlooked an ornamental fish pond and the cooling pond (foreground) for the recirculating laboratory cooling water. The block on the right housed the building's engineering services and other amenities. Copyright © QinetiQ plc

The front entrance of M-Building, with engineering service facilities, plant rooms, storerooms and workshops to the left, and the Registry and EMU office to the right. On the upper floor, between the service voids linking the laboratories, there was a kitchen, tea room and seminar room with a library annexe. Copyright © QinetiQ plc

A recirculating, de-ionised and filtered water supply was installed to extract heat from the large number of crystal pullers and other power-hungry equipment. Heat exchange via an external pond allowed five hundred kilowatts to be dissipated under the least favourable weather conditions using sprays to aid evaporation. An adjacent ornamental pond gave staff the pleasure of seeing fish (initially tended by Kathy Fairhurst) swimming around outside their office windows. The cost of the new materials building was £700,000, equivalent to around nine million pounds on 2012 prices.

M-Building was formally opened on Friday, 30 April 1971 by the Right Honourable Lord Hinton of Bankside who, on the same day, also opened an extension to the Mathematics Building, the new Computing laboratory, N-Block. The Establishment was justly proud of its new laboratories and the time was opportune to display its leading edge facilities to the outside world. The Press was invited on site to view the two new buildings and their facilities on the Wednesday and Thursday before the official opening ceremony on Friday. Close family visited on the Saturday and there was an open day for 120 visitors on the Monday.

By the early 1970s RRE Malvern's many other visitors from across the world heaped great praise on its Electronic Materials facilities which, undoubtedly, were second to none. They were quite a magnet for new recruits, with a state of the art specialist laboratory and a first class infrastructure of support facilities. These included workshops for mechanical and electrical engineering, glass blowing (George Isaacs and Malcolm Smith) and crystal cutting and polishing (Geoff Fynn and Colin Hartwright).

Geoff Green deserves the highest accolade for his inspired work in designing M-Building's infrastructure and for his part in the commissioning of its facilities.

Automation of the crystal pullers

Initially, control of the growth of pulled crystals, particularly their shape, was carried out by skilled operators who made tiny adjustments

P4 Division staff outside M-Building c.1979. Copyright © QinetiQ plc

(1) Brian Cockayne, (2) Bill Bardsley, (3) Don Hurle, (4) Phil Haggar, (5) Olly Jones,
(6) Robin Farrow, (7) Gordon Jones, (8) Jim Savage, (9) Marjorie Cole,
(10) Ritchie MacEwan, (11) Gordon Wilson, (12) Gordon Joyce, (13) Hugh Woodyatt,
(14) Peter Born, (15) Steve Aldridge, (16) Ken Marsh, (17) Andy Pitt, (18) Rob Series,
(19) Keith Barraclough, (20) Malcolm Smith, (21) Ted Bullen, (22) David Marshall,
(23) Phil Smith, (24) Graham Brown, (25) Peter Smith, (26) Denys Gasson,
(27) Iain Young, (28) Brian Lent, (29) Mike Houlton, (30) Hugh Webber,
(31) Doug Coates, (32) Nigel Chew, (33) Janet Firth, (34) Gordon Rae, (35) David Lee,
(36) Gerald Williams.

to the power supplied to the heaters in order to effect changes in crystal diameter. This required skill, patience and attention over long periods. A problem arose with Brian Cockayne's programme of oxide crystal growth because the maximum growth rate that could be employed in the growth of these materials was very much lower than could be used for semiconducting crystals of similar size. For oxides this was of the order of one millimetre per hour compared with several cms per hour for silicon and germanium. In consequence twenty-four-hour shift working was necessary so there was a great need to automate the process.

Geoff Green conceived the idea of weighing the crystal as it grew and inferring the crystal diameter from the rate of change of that weight. A simple servo-mechanism compared the rate of increase of the weight with the expected rate for a given required crystal diameter and growth speed; the difference (the 'error' signal) was used to make the necessary small adjustments in heater power. This worked well for oxide crystals but when Geoff tried it for the growth of germanium something unexpected happened. Rather than producing a crystal with constant diameter, the diameter oscillated wildly and periodically. Don Hurle made a study of the problem and discovered that it arose from two properties of the semiconductors not possessed by the oxides. These were a) their melts are denser than their crystals (the opposite is true for almost all other materials except water) and b) their melts do not completely 'wet' the crystal. As was expected, this anomalous effect was subsequently found also to occur for silicon and the III-V compounds.

Design of a servo-controller to address this problem required knowledge of the dynamics of the pulling process, i.e. the growing crystal's response to small changes in pulling speed and melt temperature. This is termed its transfer function (TF) which was not known at the time. Don derived theoretical equations that predicted the form of the TF. Gordon Joyce, with the assistance of Gordon Wilson, experimentally determined values of the parameters in the theoretical model. In addition, on contract, Anna Crowley at the

Royal Military College of Science (RMCS) at Shrivenham carried out a computer simulation of the growth of a crystal following small disturbances. These three approaches proved mutually consistent and, armed with that information, the two Gordons developed a servo-controller specifically designed to deal with the problem of the 'anomalous' response. Phil Tufton used the system for LEC growth of indium phosphide, obtaining excellent and consistent control over crystal shape. Gordon Joyce and Kim Turner went on to install it on other crystal pullers in the Division. The servo-controller delivered more precise and consistent control than could be achieved by even the most skilled operators. This improved the uniformity and perfection of the grown crystals as well as removing the need for continuous human monitoring. Later, Kathy McKell produced software to digitise the original analogue system.

The automation of the pulling process was ground-breaking work. It revealed for the first time the dynamics of the pulling process. The servo-controller was patented and licensed to Metals Research (MR). Gordon Joyce tested the performance of their manufactured version and MR marketed it world-wide with their 'Malvern' puller.

Crystal defect and device characterisation

Vital to improving the quality and performance of crystals and the devices made from them, is the ability to characterise their properties. For electronic materials this is a very wide field. There are core techniques such as optical microscopy for studying defects exposed by chemical etching; there are also techniques for measuring electrical and optical properties that are applicable to semiconductors. Most of these are inexpensive enough and simple to operate such that each section had its own facility. But, as the technologies advanced, properties at dimensions corresponding to sub-optical wavelengths (less than about 0.0004 millimetres) became the focus for study. The tools required for this are neither inexpensive nor simple to use. Electron microscopy[G] and X-ray imaging[G] techniques are amongst these and, to meet the Division's needs, state of the art equipment was required.

A scanning electron microscope[G] (SEM) was purchased in the mid 1960s and used to determine the spatial distribution of chemical composition in materials. In 1967 Doug Coates made the discovery that, under certain operating conditions, SEM reflection patterns were formed superimposed on the topographic images of crystalline materials. These patterns could be used to determine crystal orientations of microscopic regions of the specimen. This discovery significantly enhanced the capability of the SEM and attracted international interest. The patterns are now often referred to as 'Coates Patterns'. The scanning electron microscopy capability was further strengthened in the early 1980s when Dorcas Dosser moved from Baldock (chapter seven) and Colin Warwick, an expert in cathodoluminescence,[G] was recruited from Oxford University.

A state of the art transmission electron microscope[G] (TEM) was

Tony Cullis adjusting the imaging conditions of the new transmission electron microscope (c.1979). Copyright © QinetiQ plc

purchased when Tony Cullis, an Oxford D.Phil. left Bell Laboratories to join the Division in 1975. The TEM enabled him to study crystal defects on the near atomic scale (the order of 0.000001 millimetres) of many bulk and layered materials. With it, he was the first person to identify micro-precipitates and micro-voids in melt-grown gallium arsenide crystals. Tony, assisted by Nigel Chew, Peter Smith and Gerald Williams, together with the SEM staff, gave critical feedback on detailed materials structures and defects to personnel working on materials and device characterisation in Physics Group. One example is his assistance to Leigh Canham to show that the luminescence of highly porous silicon (chapter nine) originated from crystalline nanostructures[G] and that these were responsible for efficient light emission.

In addition Tony pursued his own fundamental studies. One notable such study in the late 1970s arose from news that emerged from the Soviet Union of the use of very rapid pulses of laser light to anneal the damage produced when dopant atoms were implanted at high energy into silicon wafers to fabricate discrete devices and integrated circuits.[G] Immediately, research on this started all around the world and, with the support of Hugh Webber, Tony rapidly established a facility to replicate the Soviet work. The major experimental problem was how to improve the attainable spatial uniformity of the intensity of the laser beam. Tony quickly solved this problem, giving him a world-leading position in the field. This enabled him, in collaboration with John Poate at Bell Laboratories, to determine that the annealing of layers was the result of the melting of the surface which then recrystallised at a speed of several metres per second. That is almost a million times faster than obtainable with conventional melt growth techniques. Together they then studied the enhanced solubility of dopant atoms obtained at these enormous speeds and showed that this matched the observed 'annealing' behaviour. Prior to this work the idea of surface melting had been strongly disputed by some laboratories: Tony and John's work settled the matter unequivocally.

X-ray diffraction[G] techniques to determine the orientation of the crystal axes with respect to the surface of a crystal wafer were available from the outset but initially the Division lacked more specialised techniques. Gordon Jones moved to the X-ray area in about 1977 to develop techniques for the measurement of the spacing of atomic layers (lattice parameter) and single crystal analysis. In collaboration with Professor Michael Hart, (King's College, London), he pioneered the use of double crystal X-ray topography[G] for the evaluation of bulk single crystals and epitaxial layers. With support from Ken Lloyd, Gordon made structural analysis of a wide range of materials including hetero-epitaxial layers grown by Robin Farrow by Molecular Beam Epitaxy (see chapter ten), as well as materials provided externally such as natural and synthetic quartz. (The Division did not grow these large quartz crystals but characterised material from external contractors responsible for meeting defence procurement requirements).

In 1978 Graham Brown was recruited from Birmingham University to work with Brian Cockayne and Ritchie MacEwan on the characterisation of LEC indium phosphide substrates using a variety of techniques, including infrared microscopy, X-ray topography[G] and both scanning and transmission electron microscopy.[G]

By the early 1980s the non destructive technique of double crystal X-ray diffraction[G] had become one of the most powerful tools for the analysis of III-V multilayer structures that were of increasing interest to the Physics Group for a whole host of potential new devices (chapter ten). There was also increasing interest in imaging two- and three-inch-diameter wafers of gallium arsenide to understand the role of defects in the electrical behaviour of substrates fabricated from semi-insulating crystals (chapter three). This was part of a collective UK effort within the Gallium Arsenide Consortium to investigate the use of direct ion implantation[G] into these substrates to make field effect transistors[G] (chapter eight). Graham's X-ray work was initially supported by Iain Young (the son of CMT pioneer Alex Young) and by the recruitment of Steve Barnett from Brian Tanner's group at the University of Durham. Later, Andrew Keir joined the team. In-house work was also complemented by accessing the powerful synchrotron[G] source at Daresbury, a key facility for imaging the structure of whole wafers using X-rays. The X-ray group made significant contributions to the understanding of the role of dislocations[G] in determining the electrical properties of semi-insulating gallium arsenide; it also helped eradicate an important defect related to dislocations in indium phosphide, known as 'grappes'.

Most elusive of all the defects to be found in crystals are the point defects, i.e. defects on the scale of a single atom. These are present, in equilibrium, in all crystals at all temperatures above the absolute zero of temperature. In the case of elemental crystals such as silicon, there are vacant atom sites ('vacancies') and atoms not on a lattice site ('self interstitials'). In silicon these are present in melt grown crystals in concentrations of the order of only one part in ten million but, nonetheless, they can have a profound effect on device performance, especially if they aggregate to form extended defects (chapter nine).

Compound semiconductors, such as the III-V compounds are more complicated. There are vacancies on both the Group III and Group V sub-lattices and interstitial atoms of both types also. Further, Group III atoms can sit on Group V sites and vice versa ('antisite defects'). Complications also arise from the fact that, under certain conditions, some or all of these defects can become electrically charged, particularly when electrically active dopants are added to the crystal. The concentration of some of these defects in the common III-V compound semiconductors (for example gallium arsenide and indium phosphide) can be as high as one part in five thousand.

Don Hurle pioneered the use of thermodynamic theory to describe the formation of, and the reactions between, these defects. Amongst several discoveries, he was able—with colleagues from the Division and from Trent Polytechnic, Plessey and ICI Wafer Technology—to explain how a certain defect, known as EL2 (which controlled the semi-insulating behaviour of gallium arsenide), was formed. This occurred not during growth, but during cooling of the crystal to room temperature. They were able to show how post-growth annealing of the crystal could be used to optimise and homogenise the EL2 concentration.

As the range of devices increased and they became ever smaller and more sophisticated, there were demands for improved characterisation techniques. By the mid 1980s, ability to measure low concentrations of dopants in thin semiconductor layers had become vital. The appropriate technique—secondary ion mass spectrometry[G] (SIMS)—was available at the Admiralty Research Laboratories, Holton Heath, Dorset. Steadily increasing usage of this capability by RSRE staff led to the equipment being transferred to P4 Division in 1983, along with its expert operators, Graham Blackmore and Steve Courtney. Similarly, electrical characterisation of very thin layers posed new problems which were addressed by Mike Young and David Lee in P4 Division. By the end of 1987, over 40 per cent of the staff of the Division (some twelve people) were deployed in the characterisation area.

Another major defect that is prone to occur during the pulling of indium phosphide and some other common semiconductor crystals is the growth twin. Small facets parallel to the close packed planes in the crystal lattice form at discrete points around the periphery of the growth interface (as described for indium antimonide in chapter two). Growth on these facets occurs by two dimensional nucleation and, very occasionally, a nucleus forms with an orientation that is rotated by sixty degrees with respect to the facet. As the nucleus spreads, this new orientation is propagated throughout the crystal. This is a growth twin and its occurrence usually makes the crystal useless for device purposes. No explanation had been found for this effect since it was first noted in the 1950s. In 1987, developing an idea by V. Voronkov, Don Hurle established theoretically the conditions under which such a nucleus could form that was actually thermodynamically favoured over an untwinned one. Colleagues in German and USA laboratories later experimentally tested his predictions and found good agreement. In particular, reasons for its prevalence in indium phosphide are now understood and Don was able to define conditions that minimised the risk of such twinning. At long last there was a scientific explanation for the formation of this troublesome defect.

Infrared window materials

As infrared detecting devices became applied in advanced sensor systems, the requirement arose to mount them in missile trackers and on fast jet aircraft fitted with a durable infrared window material. Calcium aluminate glass domes already existed for missiles directed at high temperature targets such as missile and jet engine exhausts where transparency in the 3–5 micron band was required. To protect devices in missiles targeting objects at around ambient temperature when in flight, a longer wavelength infra-red transparent window material was required. Such materials capable of withstanding the enormous stresses imposed by high velocity flight with rain impact were not available at that time.

To tackle this problem, Jim Savage, a technologist from Sheffield University who had just completed his doctorate research there, was recruited in 1962 to work with Stan Nielsen. Jim's first task was to make and determine the physical stability and properties of the 8–12 micron waveband infrared transmitting chalcogenide[G] glasses that looked promising as components for the 8–12 micron systems. With support from Ken Marsh, a study of a number of other candidate materials was also made, and vapour deposited zinc sulphide proved the best option for airborne windows. This work became of importance when, in the 1970s, the armed forces sought to improve their night vision capability by replacing their image intensifiers with thermal imaging cameras.[G] Jim sponsored work at Barr and Stroud, Cambridge University, Plessey and the Atomic Weapons Research Establishment (AWRE). The work on vapour deposited zinc sulphide and zinc selenide at AWRE was being carried out by Keith Lewis, a physical chemist from the Universities of Bristol and Oxford. In 1981 AWRE ceased to do any non nuclear research, so Keith moved to RSRE P4 Division. Jim and Keith, assisted by Andy Pitt, collaborated in the optimisation of the process which was scaled up to produce large flat plates and missile domes of high transmissivity zinc sulphide at Barr and Stroud (chapter eight).

7
THE MERGING OF THREE ESTABLISHMENTS

In the mid 1970s the decision was taken to close the Services Electronics Research Laboratory (SERL) at Baldock in Hertfordshire and the Signals Research and Development Establishment (SRDE) at Christchurch in Hampshire and to transfer their staff and equipment to Malvern. In 1976 HM the Queen and HRH the Duke of Edinburgh came to open the combined establishment, renaming it the Royal Signals and Radar Establishment (RSRE). Electronic Materials Division staff showed the Queen and the Duke a little of their work and, as Superintendent, Bill Bardsley presented Her Majesty with an array of gemstones made from synthetic crystals grown by the Division.

SERL had been established at Baldock at the end of the Second World War in 1945. Its prime purpose was to act as the in-house laboratory for the Co-ordination of Valves Department, CVD, which had been established by the Admiralty in 1938 to enhance collaboration with industry for the development of valves for communications. In 1972 CVD became the MoD Procurement Executive (PE) Directorate of Components, Valves and Devices (DCVD) which was the MoD authority for research and development contracts with industry on electronic components (chapter eight).

SERL's early work was on valves but was extended later to gas lasers and solid state technology, including the growth of crystals and applications of silicon and III-V semiconductors, notably gallium arsenide for photocathodes[G] and gallium phosphide for light emitting

Bill Bardsley talking to Her Majesty during her visit in 1976, with the Duke of Edinburgh and Roland Lees (Director) looking on. Copyright © QinetiQ plc

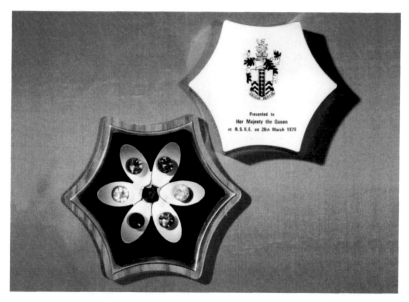

Synthetic jewels, fashioned from crystals grown in P4 Division presented by Bill Bardsley to Her Majesty. Copyright © QinetiQ plc

diodes[G] (LEDs). There were approximately twenty-five members of staff in the SERL Materials Group, led by David Marshall who returned to Malvern in late 1979 as Superintendent of P4 Division upon the retirement of Bill Bardsley from that post. Most of the scientific staff and their equipment transferred from the Baldock Materials Group to P4 Division in *c*.1980: Sidney Bass and Peter Oliver (MOCVD, chapter ten); Michael Astles, Harry Hill, Peter Wright, Verna Steward and Alison Maclean (LPE: chapter ten); Michael Young, Dorcas Dosser and Peter Rowcroft (Materials Characterisation: chapter six); Doug Brumhead (Chemistry Laboratory). In addition Don Rodway eventually moved from the Detector Research Group in RSRE Baldock to P4 Division to work on MBE (chapter ten). By *c*.1980 P4 Division consisted of more than fifty staff.

Other Baldock staff transferred their materials skills to various device divisions in Malvern at a time when materials research was being broadened beyond P4 Division (chapter fourteen). Jerry Birbeck joined the Microwave Devices and Sub Systems Division, L2 in the newly

The Services Electronics Research Laboratory, Baldock (from *SERL 1945–1976* by G. P. Wright). Copyright © QinetiQ plc

constructed P-Building, with Jerry providing epitaxial layer structures to that Division. David Wight eventually joined L2 Division after transferring from Baldock to O3, the Infrared Detector Division. Ian Blenkinsop also joined O3 Division from Baldock's Materials Group. Michael Astles and his team eventually moved from P4 to O3 Division to work on the growth of CMT by liquid phase epitaxy (chapter ten). Chris Pickering transferred from Baldock's Materials Group to P1, the Solid State Physics and Devices Division to work with Paul Dean and Maurice Skolnick on photoluminescence[G] of GaAs.

Former staff members of Baldock's Materials Group joined RSRE Malvern via Detached Duty elsewhere: Dick Griffiths worked for a year at Cornell University, USA before joining the MOCVD section in P4 but left the Service soon after; David Smith joined O2, the Imaging Systems Division via the British Embassy in Washington, USA; Michael Rowland arrived via DCVD in London and became Superintendent of O3 Division in c.1980. Brian Holeman also transferred from Baldock to O3 Division. Both Michael Rowland and Brian Holeman later became Superintendents of P4, Electronic Materials Division.

The arrival of the Baldock materials group greatly strengthened RSRE Malvern's capability on epitaxy and characterisation in P4 and other divisions at a time when the understanding of the growth of thin films was becoming increasingly important for device research (chapter ten).

8
TRANSFER OF TECHNOLOGY TO INDUSTRY

DCVD Organisation

The principal mechanism by which advances made in the Physics Group were transferred to the UK electronics industry was through the MoD (PE) DCVD organisation. DCVD had a number of research panels, the ones most relevant to the Electronic Materials Division being the General Circuits and Devices Research Panel and the Solid State Physics Research Panel, later to be renamed the Applied Physics and Materials Panel. DCVD placed research and development (R&D) contracts with the major electronics companies from which the Ministry of Defence procured electronic and optical equipment (normally via 'prime contractors'). Companies included Ferranti, Mullard/Philips, General Electric Company (GEC), Standard Telephones and Cables (STC), English Electric Valve Company (EEV), Barr and Stroud, Thorn EMI and Plessey. Materials suppliers included British Drug Houses (BDH), Metals Research/Cambridge Instruments, Mining and Chemical Products (MCP) and ICI Wafer Technology. DCVD also funded some university research, mainly at PhD and post-doctoral level. The technical content of these R&D contracts was supervised ('sponsored') principally by staff from RRE/RSRE Malvern and SERL Baldock.

A good example of successful technology transfer is the zinc sulphide deposition process for infrared windows where an in-house laboratory process was transferred to Barr and Stroud in Scotland to

Zinc sulphide infrared transparent components produced by Barr and Stroud.

make large slabs and missile domes. Each deposition run required a manifold of hydrogen sulphide gas bottles and around a quarter of a ton of zinc metal. Four slabs of material up to one metre in dimension were deposited in each run, or several tens of twenty-centimetre-diameter missile domes with suitably configured graphite substrates. This positioned Barr and Stroud as one of the leaders in the field, with success in winning major export orders for their zinc sulphide, notably for the AGM-65 Maverick missile seeker.

To achieve effective co-ordination between several contractors working in the same field and with CVD and Establishment staff, several *ad hoc* consortia were set up. Where the in-house programme was small and the prime need was co-ordination of the CVD programmes of several contractors (rather than for collaboration between the Establishment and the contractors in a joint research programme), CVD would have a single sponsor for all the related programmes. This was the case for the infrared windows programme mentioned above and in chapter six. Jim Savage chaired a Working Party, which later became the Infrared Optical Materials Committee, that oversaw that work. This mode of co-ordination was also used in the optical fibres for military communications programme when, in the 1980s, Jim sponsored contracts at GEC, STL, Thermal Syndicate and Royal Military College, Shrivenham. Additionally, he undertook liaison with US Naval Laboratories and reporting to CVD.

For major activities such as gallium arsenide large consortia were formed.

Gallium Arsenide Consortium

The first, and the most long-lived of these consortia, was the Gallium Arsenide Consortium formed in 1966 under the Chairmanship of Cyril Hilsum, then at SERL Baldock and the pioneer of research on that material in the UK. The Chairmanship passed to Brian Mullin in 1971.

Early meetings were a forum for six-monthly progress reports. The programme was principally focused on producing material that was sufficiently pure for it to exhibit the newly discovered Gunn effect which held exciting possibilities for microwave power generation, later to be realised also with indium phosphide. The inventor of the device based on this effect was Ian Gunn of IBM Research Labs in Yorktown Heights, USA, who had previously worked in the Physics Group at RRE. At that time there was no major commercial exploitation of gallium arsenide; everyone was desperately struggling with its technical problems and help from any quarter was welcomed. Funding of research in the UK was largely by CVD and was directed at meeting perceived long-term military needs.

As the scope of the work widened, sub-division into Working Parties (WPs) became necessary and Brian instituted WPs on substrates, liquid phase and vapour phase epitaxy (chapter ten). In 1975 he ceased work on gallium arsenide to undertake research on CMT and the Chairmanship passed to Don Hurle who, over the next decade, progressively developed its collaborative aspects and further extended the number of WPs.

The declared objectives of the Consortium were:

1. To bring together UK workers in the field of gallium arsenide and related materials.

2. To keep members informed of current developments in the fields of growth and characterisation.

3. To establish national collaborative programmes of pre-competitive research between industry, government laboratories and universities directed toward device-relevant goals.

4. To optimise the return from CVD funding of work on gallium arsenide and related materials.

Once the potential military importance of the gallium arsenide field effect transistor[G] and later the microwave integrated circuit[G], were perceived, CVD was keen to ensure the availability in the UK of GaAs wafers of adequate quality on which to make these devices. To this end CVD funded Cambridge Instruments to grow two-inch-diameter crystals using Brian Mullin's high pressure LEC process which had been licensed to them by RSRE.

This development coincided with the world-wide take-up of direct implantation of dopant ions into the substrate as the technology for the production of the first generation of GaAs microwave integrated circuits. Control of spatial uniformity of the properties of the implanted layer is crucial to the ability to make integrated circuit arrays and the Consortium Substrate WP (chaired by Derek Stirland from Plessey Allen Clark Research Centre, Caswell) ran two major collaborative exercises to qualify substrates. These were SISII (semi-insulating substrates for integrated circuits) and HOGAS (homogeneity of gallium arsenide substrates).

SISII established that the Cambridge Instruments crystals grown by the high pressure LEC technique had superior semi-insulating properties to material being grown by other techniques. This aided the world-wide sale of their 'Malvern' and 'Melbourn' high pressure pullers. However, this exercise, and much equivalent work around the world, also showed that the uniformity of such wafers was inadequate for the production of field effect transistor microwave integrated circuits.

The HOGAS exercise was undertaken to address this problem. Collaboration between Cambridge Instruments and the device companies (Plessey, GEC and STL), the government laboratories and universities was managed by Don Hurle in his capacity as Consortium Chairman and as sponsor of the Cambridge Instruments CVD contract. The work involved processing arrays of test device structures on whole wafers. The effect of the high density of dislocations present in LEC-grown crystals was evaluated but it became clear that the quality of the polishing of the substrate was the major issue. This problem was tackled and eventually solved. It was also discovered that the electrical resistivity and its spatial uniformity could be controlled by a specific schedule of post-growth annealing at two different temperatures.

The requirement to fabricate new GaAs opto-electronic devices moved the focus of research to epitaxial growth technology. Amongst a number of growth techniques for the production of epitaxial layers onto substrates, metal organic chemical vapour deposition (MOCVD) and molecular beam epitaxy (MBE) became the two most important ones (chapter ten).

MOCVD was covered by the Vapour Phase Working Party (chaired by David Wight, initially at SERL, then at RSRE following the merger of the Establishments). The principal focus for the work was the CVD GaAs photo-cathode programme to provide an image intensifier to improve night vision capability. A key issue was the purity of the gaseous chemicals used in the MOCVD process and there was collaboration with Epichem plc, a principal UK supplier.

An MBE WP was set up in 1983 with Colin Wood from GEC as its chairman. Colin had returned from the USA where he had acquired expertise in the technique and he assisted the nine industrial and academic groups who had recently purchased MBE equipment. MBE offered the ultimate in the control of epitaxial layer thickness—down to the level of a single molecular layer.

The above described activities of the Consortium are but a part of the collaborative work carried out. Other areas included:
a) The calibration and improvement of assessment techniques,

especially tools to map the spatial uniformity of the properties of the layer.

b) A study was made of the influence of the stoichiometry of the substrate on the properties of the layer after implantation. (A 'perfect' crystal of GaAs would have an equal number of Ga and As atoms; real crystals have slight deviations from this depending on how the crystal is grown).

c) The damage to the epitaxial layer caused by the implantation of dopant ions was the subject of a further study.

The list is a long one.

The degree of commitment, goodwill and motivation over more than a decade shown by the industrial, government and academic participants in these collaborative exercises was very impressive. It is this which made the Consortium a very cost-effective research activity. It was in fact a truly national programme of gallium arsenide materials research based on mutual trust between partners rather than on legally defined responsibilities.

With gallium arsenide having progressed from research to the production of a first generation of both discrete devices and microwave integrated circuits,[G] the need arose for collaborative activity to push forward manufacturing technology. Collaboration between industrial companies becomes harder to achieve as the research topic becomes closer to the marketable product when the companies are competing with each other for market share. But if CVD was to meet its defence needs and the UK was to obtain a significant slice of the rapidly growing market in GaAs-based devices in the face of international competition, the industry would need every bit of help it could get. Accordingly, a III-V Technology Consortium was set up in November 1981 under the Chairmanship of David Colliver. Don Hurle served on its committee representing the Gallium Arsenide Consortium.

Initially five WPs were set up. One of these was the Wafer Specification WP, chaired by Peter Mellor from the British Telecommunications Research Laboratory (BTRL). This defined a nationally agreed specification for SI wafers against which the whole industry had agreed to purchase. The next need was to devise test methods for quality assurance and contact was established with the German DIN standards organisation and the US SEMI and ASTM standards organisations as a start to establishing globally agreed wafer specifications and the tests necessary to verify them.

Don Hurle retired as chairman of the Gallium Arsenide Consortium in 1985, and its activities were folded into the III-V Technology Consortium which was reconfigured into three Working Groups: Wafer Technology (chaired by Graham Brown), Epitaxy (David Wight) and Device Fabrication (John Woodward). The combined consortium was renamed The Gallium Arsenide Technology Consortium. However, following the change to Agency status five years later the Consortium ceased to exist.

9
SILICON MELT GROWTH REVISITED

By the mid 1960s crystal growth research on germanium and silicon had declined markedly since, by that time, these materials were considered to be 'mature'. However, the continuing development of integrated circuits[G] with ever increasing speed and packing density, quantified in the famous Moore's Law,[1] exposed some limitations in the quality of the silicon starting material from commercial suppliers.

By the mid 1970s, it became known that microscopic defects are related to the aggregation of native point defects (silicon vacancies and self interstitials) together with residual oxygen and carbon impurities in the dislocation-free pulled crystals. These could result in decreased performance and yield of complex integrated circuits. The crystal properties depended not only on how the crystal was grown but, crucially, on how it was heat treated after growth and during device fabrication.

Bill Bardsley persuaded the Department for Trade and Industry (DTI) and its industrial advisors to address these problems by funding a programme of research at RSRE and to establish a UK source of expertise and prototype silicon crystals, in the absence of an indigenous merchant supplier. In 1977 Keith Barraclough, a metallurgist, joined

---

[1] Moore's Law states that as a result of shrinking the device feature size, the number of transistors on an integrated circuit chip doubles approximately every two years.

the Division to lead the bulk silicon programme, having gained experience in semiconductors at the Clarendon Laboratory, University of Oxford and the Siemens Research Laboratory in Munich. Keith was ably supported by Denys Gasson and Gordon Rae. Robert Series, a metallurgist from the University of Oxford, was also recruited to establish specialist characterisation techniques, with assistance from Daphne Kemp.

The bulk silicon programme was highly collaborative with UK industry, initially in an informal manner. Links with Mullard, Southampton were established as a source of wafering capability to transform prototype floating zone[G] and Czochralski-pulled crystals into polished wafers that could be trialled in device processing lines at Plessey, GEC, EEV, BTRL and the in-house device programmes on Charged Coupled Devices[G] and heavily doped silicon infrared detectors. The in-house programme of crystal growth research focused on the incorporation and post-growth annealing effects of native and impurity point defects. For this work the group gained an international reputation through its involvement in international standards meetings (DIN, SEMI) and international conferences, notably the regular meetings of the Electrochemical Society (USA), which at that time was the focal point for dissemination of the latest developments in silicon technology. Collaboration with a UK Small and Medium Enterprise company, Crystalox Ltd was also established in a DTI-funded project aimed at scaling up the melting of silicon using low frequency induction heating, a technique which eventually found its way into a process for manufacturing large directionally solidified silicon ingots for photovoltaic applications such as roof-top solar cell arrays. At the time of the flotation on the London Stock Exchange in 2007, PV Crystalox Solar was one of the world's biggest 'pure play' manufacturers of Multicrystalline Silicon for solar cells.

Informal interactions were established with leading university physics groups on the characterisation of silicon crystals, notably Ron Newman's infrared group at the University of Reading and Ed Lightowlers' group on photoluminescence[G] at King's College, London.

Gordon Rae removing a dislocation-free silicon single crystal from a commercial puller (c.1979). Copyright © QinetiQ plc

One of Ed's students, Leigh Canham, an expert in photoluminescence of silicon, was eventually recruited to the silicon team which produced a novel 1.3 micron infrared LED in prototype high-carbon silicon single crystals. Later, Leigh went on to make two major discoveries in nanostructured silicon which added novel functionality to this ubiquitous material: the efficient emission of visible light at room temperature (1990) and the preparation of biodegradable silicon (1995). These discoveries have had significant academic—(>15,000 citations) and commercial impact (multiple company formation).

The Alvey programme, 1983–1988

The Japanese had forged ahead on Information Technology (IT), with collaborative programmes on VLSI (Very Large Scale Integration) Technology in 1975 and their Fifth Generation Computer in 1982. UK was being left behind, and in 1983 it launched the Alvey programme, a five-year, £350 million pre-competitive research programme on IT between, industry, universities and government laboratories. The Alvey programme aimed to catch up on the key enabling technologies: VLSI Technology and Design, Software Engineering, Intelligent Knowledge Based Systems, Man Machine Interface and Large Scale Demonstrators.

Industry was required to fund 50 per cent (£150 million) of its contribution; the remaining £200 million was provided by DTI, MoD and the Science and Engineering Research Council (SERC). Such an all-embracing programme had significant implications for RSRE staff who became engaged in many Alvey activities. In the field of silicon materials and characterisation, for example, Keith Barraclough had multifarious roles: chairman of the Silicon Materials Working Group; member of the Silicon VLSI committee which reviewed project proposals; and project participant on bulk silicon crystal growth (Alvey Project 022—see below).

The Alvey programme established a UK IT community by bringing together around five thousand researchers from industry, academia and the research establishments in more than three hundred projects, of which 192 were full collaborations and 117 were academic-only projects monitored by an 'industrial uncle'. There was a significant overhead cost in establishing the formalities of the full collaborative projects, notably the arrangements on Intellectual Property, but the broadening of the IT base, the enhanced networking and greater visibility of the UK IT community to the rest of the world were positive aspects of the programme. There were also many individual technical successes, as described below but, sadly, the Alvey programme had little impact on the overall long term competitiveness of the UK in chip manufacture.

The growing problem of melt convection

The in-house silicon crystal growth programme became focused on studies of the effects of convection[G] in the melt, a fundamental but complex feature of crystal growth from the melt, involving various components, of which thermal convection and forced convection are the most significant. Temperature gradients in the melt are a fundamental requirement of crystal pulling, resulting in heat and mass transfer by buoyancy driven, thermal convective flow. Mechanical rotation of the crystal and the crucible container leads to forced convective flows which interact with the thermal convective flows in complex and unpredictable ways. Melt convection usually serves to mix the melt and is, therefore, a possible means of overcoming deleterious effects such as those arising from constitutional supercooling[G] in the growth of heavily doped semiconductors (chapter two). On the other hand, convective flows may lead to unwanted oscillatory effects and, in large melts, to turbulence. This produces uncontrollable changes in melt temperature and non uniformities of impurities and point defects in the growing crystal, as a result of the changes in microscopic growth rate. In silicon crystal pulling, convection plays a particularly important role in the transport of oxygen impurities from the silica crucible to the crystal growth interface but this was little understood in the mid 1970s, and became a key thrust of the in-house research programme. However, there was a continuing need to increase the silicon wafer size which meant that ever larger silicon crystals had to be grown from ever larger melts contained in ever larger crucibles. Since the nature of fluid flow in a heated container is very strongly dependent on its dimensions, it became increasingly important to control melt convection in the pulling process without discarding any of its advantages.

Don Hurle had gained an international reputation for his fundamental studies of the effects of convective instabilities on crystal growth from the melt, long before modelling using powerful computers became possible. Little was understood about the behaviour of liquid metals and semiconductors in the early 1960s, although Ken Hulme and Brian Mullin had demonstrated in 1958 that a rotating three-phase electromagnetic field could induce stirring in molten indium antimonide. In 1966 Don investigated the effects on an InSb crystal of a transverse DC magnetic field imposed on its tellurium-doped melt when growth was performed in a horizontal boat. He showed that temperature oscillations in the melt could be eliminated by the field and that, if this were done, non-uniformities in tellurium concentration ('striations') in the crystal were also eliminated (*magnetic damping*). He further showed that the temperature oscillations occurred even in the absence of a crystal: they were in fact due to oscillations in the natural convective flow in the melt. (Little note was taken of this result until a decade and a half later when *transition to chaos* in convective systems became a hot topic of research). Don, with Eric Jakeman and Roy Pike from the Theoretical Physics section, carried out a number of theoretical studies of natural convective flow in crystal growth configurations and they also calculated the response of a doped crystal to melt temperature fluctuations from which they obtained criteria for minimising dopant inhomogeneity.

Shaped magnetic fields and Alvey project 022

The application of magnetic damping to semiconductor crystal growth was not taken up until 1980 when the Sony Corporation in Japan reported silicon crystal pulling from the melt in a horizontal DC magnetic field. Following this, the RSRE programme became strongly focused on optimising the process of magnetic damping in a modified commercial-scale silicon puller.

The modified commercial silicon puller with superconducting solenoid magnets around the growth chamber, designed to produce a shaped magnetic field in the melt.

RSRE's Alvey research project culminated with the invention, by Robert Series and Keith Barraclough, of the shaped field process which was eventually patented in UK, Germany, Italy, USA and Japan. The invention specified a small vertical magnetic field component at the crystal growth interface so that the forced convective flow produced by the rotating crystal remained undamped whilst the bulk of the melt was subjected to a sufficiently large magnetic field to damp the thermal and forced convective flow close to the crucible wall. This idea combined the advantages of maintaining the excellent radial uniformity of dopants attainable in standard pulled crystals using the effects of forced convection, yet simultaneously providing a means of controlling the adverse effects of thermal convection, particularly the oxygen content and microscopic non uniformities of the crystal.

RSRE's bulk silicon crystal growth programme and the Alvey programme both ended in c.1988 and there was no uptake of the shaped-field invention in the UK. However, the patent portfolio eventually became the most commercially successful of Malvern's crystal growth inventions when, many years later, it was licensed internationally for the manufacture of near-perfect, 300 mm-diameter silicon crystals, but that's another story.[2]

---

[2] *Memories of an Invention*, Keith G. Barraclough, to be published.

10
RISE IN THE IMPORTANCE OF
EPITAXIAL GROWTH AND THIN FILMS

In the early years solid state electronic and optical devices were usually fabricated directly on wafers of single crystals obtained by slicing and polishing pulled crystals. Semiconductor device structures were obtained by diffusion or ion implantation[G] of dopants into the wafers; solid state lasers were made from rods cut from the pulled crystals. The work of

Growth apparatus for the production of high purity indium phosphide layers by vapour phase epitaxy. Copyright © QinetiQ plc

the Division, therefore, was concerned mainly with the crystal growth and characterisation of bulk materials. However, the advantages of thin epitaxial layers in providing abrupt changes in dopant concentration were gradually realised in the fabrication of many early semiconductor devices. Deposition of thin polycrystalline films also became increasingly important as interconnects and protective layers in device fabrication and also for hard, durable coatings in applications such as infrared sensors.

The progressive reduction in the size of individual devices (as described by Moore's Law) resulted in ever faster computer speeds and an ever increasing amount of information stored on a semiconductor chip. This trend is still continuing as demonstrated by today's widely used smart phone (2014). The ability to reduce the size of a device requires tighter control of the fabrication processes which, in turn, requires refinement of the epitaxial growth processes and the development of more sophisticated characterisation techniques. This chapter charts those developments at RSRE and is unavoidably the most technical chapter in the book.[1]

Initially, chemical vapour epitaxy, (CVE), from volatile halides[G] was the dominant epitaxial growth technique. Stan Nielsen, George Rich and John Filby were growing silicon layers by chemical vapour epitaxy in the mid 1960s. Later, Brian Mullin and David Ashen grew GaAs layers by chemical vapour epitaxy. In the late 1960s, Brian and David Joyce (a chemist, who joined the Division from Westinghouse Electric, Maryland, USA in 1965) used phosphorus trichloride to grow the first indium phosphide layers for high frequency microwave devices based on the Gunn effect. This work was later continued by Chris Clarke, Lesley Taylor and Bill Wilgoss in P1 Division, where device physics and fabrication were pursued. At that time RSRE had a world lead in this field.

The range of potentially useful semiconducting materials expanded rapidly and, along with it, there came ever more sophisticated devices. Early examples were the semiconducting laser and the light emitting

---

[1] Non-scientific readers will probably find this chapter very challenging. We have found it necessary to include the material if the book is to describe adequately the work and achievements of the Establishment in this field.

diode[G] (LED) made from III-V semiconducting compounds. These required multiple thin layers of more than one semiconductor or solid solutions of two or more different semiconductors (e.g. gallium indium arsenide $Ga_xIn_{1-x}As$). Each layer needed to be single-crystalline and epitaxially related to its neighbours. Initially, this was performed by liquid phase epitaxy (LPE). In the most used variant of this method it was carried out by sequentially sliding a number of reservoirs each containing a molten alloy that, when solidified on the substrate, would form a layer of the required chemical composition to make the device. Layer thickness was controlled by controlling the substrate temperature and by the duration for which the substrate and reservoir remained in contact. A particular disadvantage of LPE, compared with lower temperature processes such as MBE and MOCVD (see below), was its inability to produce extremely thin layers with sharp interfaces. However, LPE proved useful for cadmium mercury telluride (CMT), and the process was taken up in O3 Division by Michael Astles and colleagues in the early 1980s in collaboration with Mullard, Southampton, who eventually used the technique in production. (At about the same time, Tony Vere and Dennis Williams evaluated the preparation of bulk CMT by a pressurised cast-recrystallisation-anneal[G] technique).

Whereas chemical vapour epitaxy based on silane (SiH_4) and the chlorosilanes has remained the core technique for the growth of thin silicon layers, two completely new techniques and their variants were developed for advanced compound semiconductor devices requiring extremely thin layers: metal organic chemical vapour deposition (MOCVD) and molecular beam epitaxy (MBE). In the USA the former is more usually known as organo-metallic vapour phase epitaxy (OMVPE) or MOVPE. RSRE made significant contributions to the development of CVE, MOCVD/MOVPE and MBE.

Metal Organic Chemical Vapour Deposition, MOCVD

In this method of growth the metallic element is carried to the vicinity of the growth surface in the form of a volatile organic compound. This is usually tri-methyl gallium in the case of gallium arsenide, for example. This compound decomposes as it approaches the heated substrate and finally on the substrate itself to release the gallium which diffuses to surface steps and becomes incorporated into the crystal. The arsenic is carried to the surface in an inorganic form, for example as arsine (AsH_3). MOCVD was a key development for the vapour phase growth of aluminium compounds such as AlGaAs. Today, it is the major technique for the production of a wide range of electronic and optoelectronic compound semiconductor devices.

Gallium arsenide, indium phosphide and related compounds

Sidney Bass, assisted by Peter Oliver, designed and developed a research scale MOCVD reactor in 1974 when at SERL, Baldock, using it to grow layers of gallium arsenide with trimethyl gallium and arsine as precursors.[G] They demonstrated the ability to make quite pure layers

Peter Oliver assembling the original Sidney Bass-designed MOCVD reactor.
Copyright © QinetiQ plc

and also semi-insulating ones doped with chromium, ones doped with electrically active dopants and AlGaAs layers. The equipment was licensed to Metals Research who marketed it worldwide. MOCVD of GaAs/AlGaAs structures for photocathodes[G] was continued by Peter Oliver on his move from Baldock to Malvern in 1980. Sidney Bass continued to work in the field but now growing high purity indium phosphide in support of the P1 Division work on microwave devices. With assistance from Lesley Taylor in P1, he made a detailed study of the dependence of the device performance on the conditions of growth. He collaborated with Epichem Ltd., suppliers of the precursors, in searching for possible new precursors to replace the highly toxic arsine and phosphine used initially. Sidney later built a computer-controlled MOCVD reactor which could grow a whole range of compounds with a capability of controlling layer thickness down to only a few atoms.

Cadmium mercury telluride

In *c.*1975 Brian Mullin started research on the growth of epitaxial layers of CMT by Metal Organic Vapour Phase Epitaxy (MOVPE). He was joined in 1978 by a newly recruited materials scientist, Stuart Irvine, from Birmingham University. Careful consideration of the organic alkyl precursors of the constituent elements to be used was needed along with handling a relatively high vapour pressure of mercury. Very pure precursors are crucial to the success of the process. The commercially available ones had about one part per hundred of impurities and, for success, this had to be reduced to around one part per million! In collaboration with David Cole-Hamilton and Tony Jones at Liverpool University this was achieved by forming and purifying an adduct[G] of the precursor followed by recovery and further purification of the precursor. Tony Jones was introduced to Epichem Ltd, (a recently formed company whose main business at that time was the production of silane for the silicon electronics industry). He joined the company and they manufactured and marketed the purified adduct under licence. Using these adducts Janet Hails, Stuart and Brian developed a technique for growing CMT layers on gallium arsenide substrates.

Another novel step in the process was pioneered by Stuart and Brian. This made use of the very high rate of inter-diffusion of mercury and cadmium in CMT. With Jean Giess (née Tunnicliffe), they grew very thin, alternate layers of CdTe and HgTe which inter-diffused during the growth process to give an alloy of spatially uniform composition. The mercury to cadmium ratio was controlled by the relative thickness of the alternating layers. They also devised a novel method for achieving growth at lower temperatures, based on the use of ultra-violet light to stimulate the decomposition of the organic precursor—a process known as photo-enhanced or photolytic decomposition, also researched by Tony Vere, supported by Don Rodway and Kevin Mackey, for the photo-assisted growth of gallium arsenide.

Zinc and cadmium chalcogenides

Structures comprising many (order of 100) layers alternating between two compounds, each only a few atom layers thick held promise for a new class of semiconducting lasers. Examples are zinc sulphide/zinc selenide (ZnS/ZnSe) and zinc selenide/cadmium selenide (ZnSe/CdSe). Brian Cockayne, joined by Peter Wright when he moved to Malvern from Baldock in 1980, grew such structures. They pioneered new pure metal organic adducts and licensed Epichem Ltd. to manufacture and market them.

Molecular Beam Epitaxy, MBE

In this method each element is separately placed in an oven containing a small orifice oriented such that atoms or molecules of vapour emerging from it are directed toward a heated substrate. In the case of GaAs this would be as atoms of gallium and molecules of arsenic (As_2 and As_4). The whole is enclosed in a chamber that is evacuated down to an extremely low pressure, such that the beams of atoms reach the crystal surface with only a small chance of having been deflected by collision with a molecule of the residual gas. Whilst MOCVD dominates commercially, MBE is coming into use where the ultimate control of layer thickness and low growth temperature (to avoid intermixing of adjacent layers) is required. R&D on the technique remains strong today (2014).

Robin Farrow was a pioneer of UK work on MBE in the early 1970s. With support from Gerald Williams and then Phil Sullivan, he produced layers of a number of materials important to the Physics Group programme including CMT, the alpha phase of tin, barium fluoride, indium phosphide and gallium arsenide. He carried out a fundamental study of the kinetics of dissociation of arsenic tetramer molecules (As_4) into dimers (As_2) during the gallium arsenide growth process and the effects associated with this on the growth behaviour. Robin also established the temperature at which gallium arsenide evaporates congruently, that is the temperature at which gallium and arsenic atoms evaporate at the same rate. All this was key to understanding and controlling the growth process. In c.1981 Robin left for the USA to continue work in the MBE field.

RSRE's first (mid 1970s) Molecular Beam Epitaxy equipment, designed and manufactured in the Establishment's workshops using some components supplied by VG Ltd. Operating it are Gerald Williams (on left) and Robin Farrow. Copyright © QinetiQ plc

An expanding programme and hybrid techniques

By the early 1980s it became clear that MOCVD and MBE were complementary techniques of major importance to the future of the Establishment's programme and, following the departure of Robin Farrow, Colin Whitehouse moved from P1 Division to lead the MBE work as part of a new initiative on low dimensional structures (LDS). Colin had joined the Establishment in 1980 from Newcastle University where he had been a post-doctoral Fellow; he had also been a materials researcher at GEC Hirst Research Centre. Trevor Martin was recruited to join him in 1985, closely followed by Chris McConville, Gilbert Smith and Andy Johnson. Trevor had just completed a PhD study of the MBE growth of indium phosphide at Glasgow University. In the following years, the Division grew low dimensional structures by MBE for research into the fabrication of a range of new electronic and optoelectronic devices being studied in the device divisions.

By the time DRA came into existence in *c.*1990, a world-leading project had started in P4 Division to build an MBE growth system coupled to the Daresbury synchrotron[G] X-ray source for real-time studies of how each crystal layer formed and how the elastic stress between neighbouring GaAs/InGaAs layers was relieved. This was a collaborative project jointly funded by MoD and SERC, with Colin as principal investigator working alongside staff at Daresbury and Brian Tanner's group at Durham University.

Perceived limitations of MBE were the requirement to open the vacuum chamber to reload sources and the absence of a selective growth process. To overcome these restrictions the concept of replacing the elemental MBE sources with the gaseous sources used in MOVPE was developed. The gaseous sources carry the elements as a molecular beam to the crystal surface where, depending on the surface temperature and chemistry, they can decompose to release the constituent atoms which are then incorporated. This technique enabled sources to be changed outside the vacuum and, because of the surface specific decomposition of the metal organic sources, true selective area epitaxy became possible.

Depending on which constituent is delivered in this way, the

MOCVD and MBE groups' staff c.1991. From left to right, front row: Dennis Soley, Val Stimson, Colin Whitehouse, Paul Moores, Richard Freer; back row: Martin Emeny, Steve Barnett, Tony Pitt, Trevor Martin, Jerry Birbeck, Sidney Bass, Peter Wright, Gilbert Smith, Andy Johnson. Copyright © QinetiQ plc

technique is known as either metal organic MBE (MOMBE) or as chemical beam epitaxy (CBE). A further enhancement of the technique is to assist the decomposition of the adduct by using a light beam of a particular frequency (photochemical epitaxy). In 1987 Trevor initiated the design and construction of a Molecular Beam Mass Spectrometer[G] (MBMS) for CBE and MOMBE growth. Penny Lane joined Colin and Trevor on this work in 1988. In 1990 they published the first study of MBMS during MOMBE growth of GaAs/AlGaAs structures. Collaboration with Epichem and with BTRL on CBE and MOMBE was also started.

Silicon epitaxy

The exciting potential of MBE to study surface physics and to enable the growth of novel structures for new devices had not gone unnoticed by the silicon community and in the early 1980s Bill

Bardsley established a programme on silicon MBE with support from Denys Gasson and Rob Hardeman. Following Bill's retirement in 1983, the silicon epitaxy team was led by David Robbins, a chemist educated at the Universities of Cambridge and East Anglia, with post-doctoral research experience at the University of Oxford. David had worked on phosphors in P1 Division and had also spent a year as a Visiting Scientist at IBM's T. J. Watson Research Centre at Yorktown Heights, USA.

MBE was not readily scaleable as a silicon production technology, especially with the requirements for ever larger wafers and high throughputs. Consequently, David, with support from Iain Young and John Glasper, by then members of SP1 Division, (chapter fourteen), developed a low pressure-low temperature chemical vapour epitaxy capability using a silane gas source within a reactor which could provide extremely low background pressures. The combination of low temperature and low pressure gave control of epitaxy thickness on the nanoscale, comparable with MBE layers, thus opening up the possibility to grow a range of structures for novel silicon devices.

Chris Pickering introduced laser light scattering and spectroscopic ellipsometry[G] onto the reactor, in order to understand and control the growth of the layers, particularly during the early stages. *In situ* optical techniques had been used in the earlier silicon MBE system and the techniques were also transferred successfully to MBE growth systems for III-V semiconductors. *Ex situ* characterisation techniques, notably Atomic Force Microscopy[G] and Scanning Optical Microscopy,[G] were used by Alan Pidduck, with support from Vish Nayar in the Silicon Processing Laboratory, to study the quality of the substrate-layer structures. Yee Leong applied specialist electrical characterisation techniques to understand the distribution of electrical dopant atoms in the layers.

As the requirements for high speed integrated circuits such as analogue to digital converters[G] became increasingly important, especially in defence applications, the application of thin silicon-germanium alloy layers in high speed heterojunction bipolar transistors[G] (HJBTs) became of considerable technological interest, once the basic growth techniques had been mastered. The RSRE team was a key partner in UK and EEC collaborations (chapter fourteen) as a supplier of prototype silicon-germanium epitaxial layers to industrial partners for the fabrication of HJBTs. Later, during the agency period, novel infra-red detectors, infrared sources and high speed FETs[G] were also fabricated in silicon-germanium layers grown at Malvern.

Other materials and techniques

Although the growth of epitaxial semiconductor layers dominated the work on thin films, there was considerable interest in other novel materials during the 1980s. When High Temperature Superconducting[G] ceramics were discovered in 1986 by IBM researchers, Müller and Bednortz, Richard Humphreys established a team at RSRE to investigate the electronic device potential of these exciting new materials. Nigel Chew left the electron microscopy team in P4 Division to establish a capability on ultra high vacuum evaporation of superconducting thin films, which included a novel oxygen source. By the early 1990s the group had established a combination of software and hardware that stabilised the composition of these complex materials more accurately than any other known group.

Keith Lewis explored the potential of MBE techniques to improve the properties of thin film optical devices in a unique system that enabled high purity sputtering[G] processes to be combined with *in situ* analytical techniques for a range of materials including chalcogenides,[G] fluorides, oxides and rare earth materials.[G] Emphasis was placed on the exploration of vanadium dioxide as a fast optical switch material, which Keith incorporated in antennae-coupled arrays, pre-empting research in the field of plasmonics[G] by at least a decade. He succeeded in gaining support from the US Air Force in the late 1980s under the Strategic Defence Initiative for the development of sensor protection techniques for space platforms, which had a significant impact on later work in the USA. His team also developed boron phosphide as a super-durable coating for external windows on airborne infrared systems, in

Boron phosphide coated missile dome. Copyright © Keith Lewis

collaboration with Pilkington Optronics (formerly Barr and Stroud). The production version of the coating was subsequently used in a number of military systems, notably Tornado, Harrrier, EFA in the UK and the F14, F15, AV-8B Harrier II aircraft in the USA. The boron phosphide coating was also applied to solve problems of corrosion encountered on electro-optic systems fitted to submarine periscopes in the UK fleet.

Later, in the 1990s Keith Lewis, Jim Savage, Don Rodway and Tim Mollart collaborated with the de Beers company to develop deposition techniques for diamond, following Alan Lettington's pioneering work on diamond-like carbon (DLC) optical coatings in the 1970s. This work culminated in the first realisation of diamond-coated missile domes.

II
ORGANISING INTERNATIONAL CONFERENCES

Advances in R&D in the field of electronic materials are immediately followed up worldwide so, to be a player in the field, a laboratory has to have a presence at international conferences where such advances are reported. If it is not also an important contributor then it will not have access to the very latest developments and will soon lose its competitive edge. Staff of P4 Division made substantial contributions to international conferences worldwide and also brought a number of major international conferences in the fields of crystal growth and defect identification to the UK.

Microscopy of semiconducting materials

In 1977, under the auspices of the Royal Microscopical Society, Tony Cullis initiated and chaired a biennial series of international conferences having this title which has continued to the present day (2014). At first they were held at Oxford, but the venue was later widened. From the outset, the conferences attracted wide international representation.

Following the organisation of the Second International Conference on Crystal Growth in Birmingham in 1968 (chapter four), a further two international meetings were organised by Division members: the Second European Conference on Crystal Growth and the Eighth International Conference on Crystal Growth.

Second European Conference on Crystal Growth
(ECCG2), 1979

Chaired by Brian Cockayne, this conference, held at Lancaster University in September 1979, was organised locally by British Association for Crystal Growth (BACG) officer, Ian Saunders and attracted two hundred and seventy five delegates. The high quality of the presentations revealed the healthy state of European crystal growth, in particular its expansion from its classical, academic past into a highly technological present. Delegates also became aware of the impressive capability of the People's Republic of China, particularly in the field of oxide crystal growth. The Chinese delegation was amongst the first scientists to be allowed to travel to the West, the Chairman Mao era having come to an end. Their excitement at being at the conference was palpable and, when they opened a large display case, delegates were presented with a view of a wide range of high temperature oxide single crystals of apparently high perfection. For some materials these were larger than had been achieved in the West at that time.

The social programme of the conference included a single-malt whisky tasting session in which some delegates engaged a little too heartily, as was evident when they finally appeared for breakfast the next morning! An alarming moment in the social programme was the temporary disappearance of two Russian delegates on Blackpool's Golden Mile. It would not have been good for government servants to have had to report to higher authority the loss of delegates from the Soviet Union during the Cold War period!

Eighth International Conference on Crystal Growth
(ICCG8), 1986

The BACG was invited to hold the Eighth International Conference on Crystal Growth (ICCG8) in 1986 along with its associated International Summer School (ISSCG6). The Summer School, organised by BACG officer Peter Dryburgh, was held in Edinburgh from 6 to 11 July 1986 and RSRE staff, Brian Cockayne, Don Hurle, Graham Brown and Keith Barraclough gave talks.

The York Railway Institute Silver Band playing in the engine turntable pit of the National Railway Museum in York on the occasion of the conference dinner during the Eighth International Conference on Crystal Growth in 1986. Copyright © Ian Saunders

At BACG's request Brian Cockayne and Don Hurle, together with Frank Ainger from Plessey, Caswell, co-chaired the conference held on the University of York campus on 13–18 July 1986. The conference was attended by 530 delegates from thirty different countries. As with ICCG2 at Birmingham in 1968, presentations by RSRE staff at the conference and visits by foreign researchers to RSRE after the conference enhanced the Division's international standing.

The social highlight of the conference was the Dinner, held in the National Railway Museum amongst the engines and rolling stock. The York Railway Institute Silver Band, hidden in the engine turntable pit, struck up vigorously as the meal started, to the considerable surprise and pleasure of the delegates.

12
STAFF ROLES AND INTERESTS

The formation of the Scientific Civil Service in 1945 had resulted in all government scientists being placed in one of three categories (known officially as 'classes' at the time): Scientific Officer, Experimental Officer and Scientific Assistant. Entry to each class was determined by scientific qualifications and an interview board; progression to different levels (grades) within each class was determined by a promotion board.

The career grade for honours graduate scientists in the early post-war period was Principal Scientific Officer, PSO (one grade lower than for the equivalent administrative grade—one recalls Winston Churchill's reported edict: 'scientists on tap but not on top'). Promotion above the career grade was into administrative posts, with the exception of a small number of staff who were deemed to be sufficiently creative researchers to merit promotion whilst continuing to work at the bench. These were named Individual Merit (IM) positions and candidates were required to submit a five-year programme of work to an examining board which consisted of eminent and mostly academic scientists having no connection with the Civil Service. Resubmission at the end of the five years could take place but if the candidate failed to impress the board he/she would be demoted to the 'substantive grade' of PSO. Within the field of crystal growth, six members of RRE/RSRE progressed by the IM route: Brian Mullin, Don Hurle and Brian Cockayne became Deputy Chief Scientific Officers (IM); Tony Cullis, Keith Lewis and David Robbins became Senior Principal Scientific Officers (IM).

In general, Experimental Officer and Scientific Assistant posts were filled by staff who were not honours graduates but had other relevant technical qualifications. Whilst the scientific officers defined the research programmes, it was the experimental officers who were at the forefront of laboratory work: they brought practical skills less likely to be possessed by scientific officers. For example, Geoff Green as a young Experimental Officer designed the crystal puller and oversaw its manufacture in the workshops. Later he conceived and implemented the use of crystal weighing during pulling to control diameter. He also planned the facilities to be incorporated in the new Materials Building and provided detailed information on the use of those facilities. In later years the experimental officer grades were abolished, leaving a single scientific officer class to which had been inserted two new grades. These were Assistant Scientific Officer (ASO) and Higher Scientific Officer (HSO) which straddled the existing Scientific Officer grade (SO).

Scientific assistants (SAs) were frequently recruited at age eighteen on completion of their A-levels. They brought valuable skills working as microscopists, crystal puller operators, making electrical and other measurements etc. Latterly, support grades also included Professional and Technology Officers (PTOs) and Experimental Workers (EWs).

In the early years there was a marked gender bias, common throughout most of physical science and engineering research and indeed of industry also. Whilst there were probably more women than men in the SA grades, there was a marked dearth of women in the S and E grades. To some extent, however, change was underway by the 1970s.

Outside the laboratory, staff contributed to many aspects of life in Malvern. Dramatic and musical interests included Scottish country dancing, acting and back-stage management, playing in local orchestras, singing in choirs and in the local Light Opera Society. Driving in rallies organised by the Civil Service Motoring Association or playing in local sports teams appealed to others.

Two members of P4 Division demonstrated exceptional talents

beyond the laboratory. Gordon Rae used his excellent engineering skills to design and build racing cars and radio controlled model aircraft. He raced his cars at circuits in the UK and, now in his eighties, is still occasionally racing and test driving. He was recently heard to say, proudly, that now Stirling Moss had handed in his racing driver's licence he, Gordon, was the oldest person in the land to hold one! Different talents have enabled Peter Smith, with his wide knowledge of and passion for literature and classical music, to contribute to the cultural life of Malvern. Almost single-handedly he has, for the last twenty-five years, organised the Autumn in Malvern Festival, each year having a different theme. He manages to attract very talented musicians and to augment this with speakers on topics relating to the theme of that year's festival. This service to the community has earned him an MBE. He is also a Fellow of the Royal Society of Arts.

More personal events have included no less than four betrothals between 'materials' staff over the years: Vivienne Doyle married Olly Jones (with whom she worked), Veronica Franks married Steve Hiscocks, Penny Lane married Peter Wright and Alison Maclean married Dennis Williams.

13
AWARDS

A number of awards has been given to sub-groups within the Division. In the period from 1979 (the first year in which government laboratories were permitted to submit) to 1992, the Establishment received no less than thirteen Queen's Awards for Technology. Six of these encompassed work on crystal growth.

The first award, in 1979, was to the Division for the development of equipment and techniques for the growth of single crystals of electronic materials. This technology was licensed to Metals Research and marketed as the 'Malvern' Czochralski System and the 'Malvern' Automatic Crystal Growth System.

The second and third Queen's Award in 1983 were awarded:

Jointly to the Division and to Hilger Analytical Ltd for research and development of crystals for the high resolution detection of X-rays and for its application in body and brain scanners.

Jointly to the Detector Research Division of RSRE and the Electro-optics Division of Mullard for the research and development of CMT infrared detectors for use in thermal imaging systems[G] in military, medical and industrial applications.

The fourth in 1987 was conferred on the Detector Research Division jointly with the English Electric Valve Company, Chelmsford for the research and development of image intensifiers with gallium arsenide photocathodes.[G] Materials research for this application had started at Baldock and continued in P4 Division, Malvern, following the merger.

Group photograph of the P4 winners of a Queen's Award for Technology in 1979.
Copyright © *Malvern Gazette*

(1) Geoff Green, (2) Brian Mullin, (3) Bill Bardsley, (4) Don Hurle, (5) Gordon Joyce, (6) Barrie Straughan, (7) Nigel Chew, (8) Denys Gasson, (9) Gordon Jones, (10) Gordon Wilson, (11) Doug Coates, (12) Gordon Rae, (13) Anne Royle, (14) Hugh Webber, (15) Olly Jones, (16) Peter Born, (17) Steve Aldridge, (18) unknown (19) Ritchie MacEwan, (20) Peter Smith, (21) Phil Smith, (22) Mike Houlton, (23) Ken Marsh, (24) Keith Barraclough, (25) Phil Haggar, (26) Tony Cullis, (27) Graham Brown, (28) David Lee, (29) Rob Series, (30) unknown, (31) Andy Pitt, (32) Jim Savage.

Some of the winners of a Queen's Award for Technology in 1990. From left to right: B. Leese (Epichem), S. Bass, B. Cockayne, P. Wright, P. Oliver and A. Jones (Epichem). Copyright © QinetiQ plc.

The fifth, in 1990, was conferred on the Division, jointly with Epichem Ltd for the development of a process for the production of high purity metal organic precursor gases for the MOVPE growth of crystals of semiconductor and optical materials.

In 1991 a sixth materials-related Queen's Award was made jointly to the Microwave Devices Division of the newly formed Defence Research Agency and STC Optical Devices Division, Paignton. The Award was for their work on high precision epitaxial crystal growth processes for advanced opto-electronic components.

In 1976 the Rank Prize for Opto-electronics was awarded to Bill Lawson, Stan Nielsen, Ernest Putley and Alex Young for their discovery and work on CMT.

In addition there have been several awards to individuals:

In 1985 Brian Mullin received from his alma mater, Liverpool University, their Distinguished Alumnus Award.

In 1987 Don Hurle was presented with the American Association for Crystal Growth Fourth International Award for 'outstanding contributions in the field of crystal growth through technical achievements, publications and presentations and through their impact, world-wide on science and technology'. In retirement in 2001, he also received, jointly with Dr Sam Coriell of the National Institute of Technology in Maryland USA, the International Organisation for Crystal Growth (IOCG) Frank Prize (honouring the name of the late Sir Charles Frank, and given for fundamental contributions in the field of crystal growth).

Also in retirement, Brian Mullin received a very long overdue recognition of his work on the growth of III-V semiconductors by the LEC process. In 2007 he was awarded the IOCG Laudise Prize (honouring the late Robert Laudise, Head of Materials at Bell Laboratories). The citation read 'For his significant contributions to crystal growth technology, especially for the creation of the high pressure LEC process, development of MOVPE growth of CMT alloys and discovery of non-equilibrium segregation at facets'.

Tony Cullis, then at Sheffield University, was elected to Fellowship of the Royal Society in 2004.

14
CHANGING TIMES

There was a progressive break-up of the old Electronic Materials Division, as it had been originally conceived. As device development programmes became more mature, vertical integration of the enabling materials work was progressively introduced within some divisions to provide a seamless transition from materials to device research. Thus, in the early 1970s, the CMT materials programme was transferred to P2, the Infrared Research and Applications Division; in the early 1980s some epitaxial growth for microwave applications became part of L2, The Microwave and Sub Systems Division. In 1983 a major reorganisation occurred across the site in response to the Alvey programme, with the formation of a new Signal Processing (SP) Group containing an Integrated Circuits Division (SP1) into which all the silicon materials work was transferred from P4 Division. Gordon Jones, the then Superintendent of P4, moved to become Superintendent of the new SP1 Division, followed by David Marshall then Keith Barraclough within the next five years. In the decade from 1979, when Bill Bardsley ceased to be P4 Superintendent, the post was occupied successively by four people: David Marshall, Gordon Jones, Brian Holeman and Michael Rowland.

Most of the basic materials work remained within M-Building and so cross fertilisation of ideas in the tea room was able to continue as before. Many M-Building staff worked alongside device groups, even if not transferred to separate divisions. Device fabrication requires many layer processing techniques such as chemical vapour deposition, electron beam deposition[G] and in-process epitaxy that had a distinct synergy with the type of work in M-Building where experts on the processes and characterisation techniques resided. Thus many activities across the site, e.g. in the Silicon Processing Laboratory (SPEL) and in many other specialist device laboratories for CMT, GaAs, surface acoustic wave[G] (SAW) devices and pyroelectric devices were drawn closer to M-Building in many programmes, including a new initiative in c.1981 on low dimensional devices in P1 Division.

The late 1980s saw the gradual easing of the Cold War, ending in the fall of the Berlin wall in 1989, at the same time as the Thatcher administration was planning a dramatic change to the way research would be commissioned in its Defence Research Establishments. Such a major change to the status quo led MoD Headquarters to ponder some basic questions: who and what are we defending against now and—more pertinently—why do we need so much research? 'Pull through' of research on electronic materials and devices into defence components was becoming inadequate to justify a large research budget; the situation was exacerbated by the continuing decline in UK's electronics industry. Major cuts were feared if the research budget was simply to be used as a means of providing MoD with the ability to be an 'intelligent customer'.

An important change also took place in the way the Establishment went about its business with defence contractors. In the traditional co-operative approach it was felt that some contract sponsors and participants in informal consortia may occasionally have been over-generous and premature in broadcasting their own ideas. This tolled the death knell for the Gallium Arsenide Consortium—and indeed the broader concept of 'UK plc'—in which complete openness and trust had been fostered between its members.

The way forward lay in more formal arrangements. By the 1980s the DTI had become an important sponsor of Malvern's materials and device research, initially in broad, cost-shared programmes, then in more formal, short term collaborative projects with industry and

Group photograph of P4 Division staff *c*.1990. From left to right, front row: Brian Cockayne, Penny Lane, Sally Matthews, Michael Rowland (Supt.), Peggy Cox, Doreen Osbourne, Audrey Parish; middle row: Andy Johnson, Steve Barnett, Tony Pitt, Peter Wright, Peter Oliver, Peter Smith, Colin Whitehouse, Gerald Williams; back row: Graham Blackmore, student(?), Ritchie MacEwan, David Lee, Paul Moores, John Besbell (student), Phil Smith, Kim Turner, Tony Cullis, Mike Houlton, Trevor Martin, Mike Crosby, Phil Haggar, Tony Vere, Kevin Mackey, John Plant. Copyright © QinetiQ plc.

universities in initiatives such as Alvey. Research programmes within the European Economic Community (EEC) became accessible in cost-shared collaborative projects such as the European Strategic Programme on Research in Information Technology (ESPRIT). Such programmes provided an excellent networking opportunity, as well as a source of additional financial support, particularly as MoD funding gradually became more and more difficult to sustain for basic materials research. Short term projects were also the way future business would be conducted with MoD and they provided an appropriate introduction to project management and, not least, the associated administrative and management overhead in establishing collaboration agreements.

By 1991 the status of RSRE and other non nuclear defence research establishments had changed to that of a 'Next Steps Agency', leading eventually to privatisation. Grant funding for MoD work ceased, to be replaced by projects funded by MoD customers via an internal Trading Fund. The ethos of the original Electronic Materials Division was gone forever. It had worked extremely effectively in the Cold War when the driving force was to ensure the defence capability of the nation on a broad front, but was not sustainable in the new, more commercially competitive era.

This history ends at this point. What happened subsequently is summarised in the Epilogue.

15
REFLECTIONS

The Physics Group of TRE/RRE/RSRE was an organisation born of the Second World War and sustained by the Cold War that followed it. This period in history coincided with the beginnings of the exciting solid state era when the regular discovery of new materials and devices could possibly lead to technological supremacy. In order to cover all possible options, research and development of a vast range of electronic and optical materials was required, alongside a materials and component industry that could exploit this research. The price of such a huge commitment by the Western Allies, particularly the USA and the UK, was high but the cost of failure was judged to be even higher.

P4 Division of RRE/RSRE had an impressive record of innovation in new materials and components and of transferring the technologies for producing them to a vibrant UK industry. This ensured that MoD was able to acquire the knowledge, the components and the systems needed to ensure the defence of the UK. However, as more and more defence platforms and systems were procured from overseas, (especially from the USA), it became more and more difficult to sustain a fully fledged R&D capability at a time when the UK electronics industry was also in decline. The problem of sustaining a large materials and device activity at Malvern was compounded by decreasing defence budgets, the increasingly diverse range of materials and devices being investigated and the increasing cost of state of the art research equipment, such as MBE systems and characterisation equipment.

Introduction of commercial principles made it particularly hard for those working on electronic materials because the majority of potential customers would be interested only in device R&D. The continued success of materials work would thus depend in large measure on the success of the Establishment's device researchers in obtaining sufficient funding to be able and prepared to allocate some of it for materials work. Inevitably, there would be less scope for speculative materials research.

What then were the ingredients of the Division's success? In the early years, when new discoveries and new devices were being made at a great pace, the P4 Division Superintendent needed to be aware of these at a very early stage. He could then initiate a modest amount of experimental work in order to be in a position rapidly to supply the new material(s) required to study the new physics or fabricate a new device. The ability to do this helped the device physics groups to establish a commanding position in the UK and to compete internationally. This approach provided a stable research environment in which individuals and small teams could establish an international reputation for their work and this, in turn, enabled the Establishment to recruit talented people. As described in chapter eight, the CVD organisation provided an effective funding mechanism to enable new technologies to be taken through the, often long, development stage in UK industry.

In this context the role played by Bill Bardsley merits note. As Superintendent of P4 Division from its formation until about 1979 he was always looking out for new discoveries and advances of potential importance to MoD that would require new or improved materials. He then endeavoured to ensure that the Division had the capability to respond to any new challenge. The ability to respond quickly and effectively to requirements for new crystals necessitated having available the major techniques for the growth of bulk crystals and epitaxial layers. Teal and Little's pulling method for growing bulk crystals of germanium and silicon was highly innovative. When Bill and Geoff Green set out to grow germanium by this method they had to devise their own equipment: there was nothing available commercially. That their design was so well engineered and the puller so versatile that it could accommodate 'drop-in' growth chambers to deal with a very wide range of materials, made it a valuable asset to the Division.

The success of P4 Division is not to be seen only in the very large number of different crystals that were grown—although this is very impressive. Another important factor was the absence of short-termism, thus allowing the Division to develop new or improved growth technologies, notably in the area of crystal pulling. It also resulted in fundamental discoveries of many of the mechanisms by which crystal defects are formed during the growth and post-growth heat treatment—and how to prevent their formation.

It is evident from this history that crystal growth requires diverse disciplines: materials science, metallurgy, inorganic and organic chemistry, solid state physics, glass technology, electrical, mechanical and servo engineering, thermodynamics and fluid dynamics. All these were covered by recruitment directly from British Universities and of UK scientists returning from abroad from such prestigious organisations as Bell Laboratories. Discoveries and innovation in science frequently occur in areas that are at the boundaries of neighbouring disciplines. That synergy is evident in some of the work of P4 Division which sat between industry and academia, enjoying the confidence and trust of both. This unique position enabled it to be effective in bringing together the research laboratories of the industrial companies with academic scientists and with the Division's staff: 'UK plc'. This advantage was exploited in the several research consortia that were formed, as described in chapters eight and nine. We now have to look to other nations such as Germany and its Fraunhofer Institutes to see how valuable an applied research organisation can still be, positioned between academia and industry.

One failing was that, by and large, the Division was not sufficiently attentive to the preservation of intellectual property rights. The science usually seemed more pressing and interesting than working through legal documents with the Patents Officer! The problem was made harder by the fact that in the early days staff had to work at third hand with the assignee of their patents through the Establishment's and Headquarters' patents officers. Initially, patents were assigned to the National Research and Development Corporation (NRDC) and latterly to the British Technology Group (BTG). In some cases NRDC and BTG were not prepared to go to the expense of defending overseas patents, resulting in both loss of potential revenue and loss of protection to UK licensees. This is reflected in the poor protection of intellectual property within the crystal pulling equipment in most of its forms. A more professional approach was taken in the commercial era.

Staff were conscious of the privileged position they held. They enjoyed excellent research facilities in an Establishment that already had a widely held reputation for its outstanding and vital work on radar during the war years. That reputation continued to grow through the post-war years, with a significant contribution made to that growth by materials research. To the satisfaction that this gave to staff was added the fact that the Establishment was located in idyllic surroundings in a delightful town at the foot of the Malvern Hills.

16
LEGACY

What, today, can be seen to owe something to the work of Malvern's Electronic Materials Division? The legacy is substantial in many aspects of crystal growth: the current application of single crystals of newly discovered *materials* grown in the Division; the current use of *equipment and techniques* developed by the Division; worldwide acknowledgement and recognition of the contributions made by members of the Division to the *science and technology of crystal growth*; and, not least, a thriving *discipline* of crystal growth which the Division helped to found and maintain.

The area in which materials research made its biggest and most important impact is undoubtedly infrared technology. The discovery of CMT and the mastery of epitaxial growth of this hazardous and difficult material made possible the realisation of the outstanding innovations in device design by Tom Elliott and colleagues which were exploited by Mullard/Philips, Southampton (later Selex ES). It led to infrared detectors of extremely high sensitivity which proved to be life-saving in conflicts such as the Falklands War and the Gulf Wars. Infrared imaging has also found a range of non military applications, for example, in surveillance, fire fighting, medical imaging and building construction. The development of this technology arose from defence needs—and much of that from work at RRE/RSRE.

Sensor protection is another field in which the Division made a lasting contribution in collaboration with industry, firstly on glassy materials, then on materials such as zinc sulphide and novel durable coating materials. This pioneering work enabled the fabrication of windows and coatings that could withstand the stresses imposed by a jet fighter. Large areas of material could also be produced to make protective domes on missiles.

As a result of the Division's developments in the technology of crystal pulling, equipment was marketed world-wide as the 'Malvern' Crystal Growth System which could be fitted with growth chambers for either high temperature oxide growth or high pressure LEC growth, then later with the 'Malvern' Automatic Diameter Control (ADC) System. Fifty years ago Malvern gave the world the technology to grow III-V compound semiconductor crystals based on the high pressure LEC technique. The estimated value of gallium arsenide devices sold in 2013 was in excess of six billion US dollars. Around 20 per cent of the world production of gallium arsenide crystals used to make those devices was grown by the LEC process.

The discovery of the effects of magnetic damping and the subsequent application of shaped magnetic fields during crystal pulling to control melt convection are now being exploited worldwide in the production of high quality twelve-inch-diameter silicon single crystals, used to make high performance silicon chips for portable electronic equipment such as tablet computers, digital cameras, smart phones and MP3 players. It is estimated that the annual value of devices produced on silicon grown by the shaped field technique and its derivatives exceeds ten billion US dollars. As crystal suppliers respond to demands for wafers of ever larger diameter, some form of magnetic damping will almost certainly be used to grow the next generation of silicon crystals, eighteen inches in diameter.

CVD and P4 Division can take some credit for the fact that, against the odds, the UK still has an indigenous manufacturer of bulk compound semiconductor crystals, albeit now relatively small on a world scale. It started with Metals Research, a company founded by two brothers, Cole, who grew and sold metal single crystals. They took a licence to manufacture first the 'Malvern' puller and then the high pressure LEC variant to produce and sell crystals made using it. Following the worldwide demand for the high pressure puller, they developed a larger version named the 'Melbourn', acknowledging the village in which they were located. In 1981 they were bought out by Cambridge Instruments (CI). CI received financial support from CVD to develop a process for the production of semi-insulating gallium arsenide that met a specification derived from the collaborative programmes of the Gallium Arsenide Consortium. However, the crystal growth side of the business did not sit well with the core activities of CI and, in 1985, the company sold this side of its business to ICI, who set up an excellent facility at Milton Keynes with the name ICI Wafer Technology. Policy changes within ICI later led to its disposal of Wafer Technology to Mining and Chemical Products. However, there followed a management buyout when it became clear that MCP lacked the financial strength to sustain it. It traded effectively under this new management and then in 1999 the business was sold to IQE (a UK company based in Newport, South Wales), a leading world supplier of epitaxial wafers.

Following its early interaction with RSRE P4 Division in the field of adducts for MOCVD, Epichem went from strength to strength to become the world's largest supplier of metal organics to the electronics industry. In 2007 it was acquired by the Sigma Aldrich Corporation of USA for $60 million to expand its worldwide business.

The change to agency status and subsequent privatisation resulted in company spin-offs that were considered to be 'non-core' to the new organisation. One of these, pSiMedica Ltd, was formed in 2000 to exploit the earlier discovery that nanostructured silicon can be made bioactive for use in healthcare applications.

The Division has an enduring legacy in the thriving discipline of crystal growth and in its national and international organisations, BACG and IOCG. The Journal of Crystal Growth is still going strong after forty-seven years, in no small measure due to the painstaking efforts by the Division's staff in its editing, peer review process and as authors of hundreds of technical papers.

The contributions to the science and technology of crystal growth by the Electronic Materials Division, RSRE Malvern live on: Bill Bardsley's vision (chapter three) has been fulfilled.

Presentation to Bill Bardsley of a silicon crystal, grown in the shape of a mace, on his retirement in 1983. From left to right: Gordon Jones, Olly Jones, Hetty Bardsley, Doug Coates, Bill Bardsley, Senior Staff Mess official, Keith Barraclough, Gordon Rac.

EPILOGUE

Defence Research Agency, DRA, 1991–1995

The Defence Research Agency (DRA) brought together RSRE, the Royal Aircraft Establishment (RAE), the Royal Armament Research and Development Establishment (RARDE), the Admiralty Research Establishment (ARE) and some of the work of the Aeroplane and Armament Experimental Establishment (A&AEE) into a single Executive Agency of the Ministry of Defence, UK's largest research and technology organisation, with Headquarters at RAE Farnborough. DRA's principal aim was to provide the expert scientific and technical services required of it, primarily by the Ministry of Defence (MoD) in the fields of strategic research, applied research, operational assessments and studies and project support. MoD customers now held the money to pay for specific projects, with milestones and deliverables over a specified time. Money changed hands via an internal Trading Fund, which allowed the DRA to make a profit. DRA was also able to trade commercially with appropriate non defence customers, with the knowledge of its true costs.

The new customer-supplier regime did not suit everybody, and several senior staff left for pastures new. Stuart Irvine left in 1990 to take up a position at the Rockwell International Science Center in California. Don Hurle took early retirement in 1991 and was followed by Danny Robertson in 1992. Colin Whitehouse left in 1993 to become a professor in the Department of Electrical and Electronic Engineering at Sheffield University. In 1995 he was joined by Tony Cullis who was also appointed to a professorial position. These departures were a loss to the overall materials capability but, in the early days of the Agency at least, Malvern's materials research continued to be at the forefront in a number of fields: light emission and bioactivity in highly porous silicon, epitaxial growth of semiconductors, HJBTs, HTS and narrow band gap semiconductors, for example.

Defence Evaluation and Research Agency, DERA, 1995–2001

The Defence Evaluation and Research Agency, DERA, was formed by the amalgamation of DRA with the Defence Test and Evaluation Organisation, the Chemical and Biological Defence Establishment and the Centre for Defence Analysis. Declining budgets and arms-length contracting made it increasingly difficult to sustain a broad materials technology base. Competition from external organisations, particularly universities, was also looming. There were various cost-cutting measures taken to improve DERA's competitiveness, but this also meant that there were fewer scientific papers written and fewer conferences attended. The international reputation of Malvern's materials research started to decline; the regular flow of Queen's Awards ceased. Acquisition of capital equipment now had to meet stringent return-on-investment criteria. In this period there was an initiative to create a national 'Dual Use' Electronic and Optical Materials Centre, EOMC, in Malvern as a partnership between government, universities and industry. However, unlike the 'Dual-Use' Structural Materials Centre at DERA Farnborough, the EOMC received little support, especially from UK's declining electronics industry. An additional problem with the EOMC concept was the inability of a government agency to raise capital. Instead, individual dual use projects with industry were introduced in which background intellectual property rights from DERA were used to develop non-defence applications such as thermal imagers built into firemen's helmets.

QinetiQ and DSTL, 2001 onwards

As a result of the Strategic Defence Review in 1998, the government committed DERA to a form of Public Private Partnership (PPP). Of the many possibilities for the way forward with PPP, the chosen option in 2001 was the formation of a profit making company with the ingenious name of QinetiQ, which was floated on the London Stock Exchange in 2006. About a quarter of the original DERA organisation, notably sensitive activities within the fields of nuclear, chemical and biological defence, remained under MoD control as part of a separate agency, the Defence Science and Technology Laboratory, (DSTL).

Despite the overall decline in the technology base, some world class capabilities remained. For example, after building on almost fifty years of research and development, the narrow gap semiconductors team established a partnership with the Intel Corporation for research into high speed, low power InSb transistors as a possible option for application in future microprocessors. Many of Malvern's residual capabilities such as the materials characterisation team worked hard to establish a good blend of defence and non defence business but suffered increasingly from the chronic lack of investment. Fragmented materials research continued until c.2010 when QinetiQ's new CEO divested its technology base and focused the business on services within the defence and security market. The remaining crystal growth and characterisation equipment was sold off by auction. A number of staff was made redundant. Some found employment in industry, universities and government laboratories; others started their own companies.

DSTL also underwent some significant but less dramatic rationalisation. In 2009 its small Malvern contingent was relocated to the headquarters at Porton Down, thus ending the presence of government-owned research capabilities in Malvern after sixty-seven years.

The original intention of PPP in 1998 had been 'to harness the opportunities offered by a public private partnership to strengthen the Defence Evaluation and Research Agency's ability to continue to provide world class scientific research well into the next century.' After it had been decided in 2001 that the favoured PPP option would be a profit making company, it took less than a decade for QinetiQ's materials technology base to disappear.

The derelict M-Building in 2014. QinetiQ changes direction: no road ahead for Materials!

GLOSSARY OF TECHNICAL TERMS

Adduct, the product of the direct addition of two or more distinct molecules to form a reaction product that contains all the atoms of all the components.

Analogue to digital converter, a device that analyses a continuously variable signal, such as the voltage from a sensor, and converts (digitises) it into discrete quantities based on binary digits (bits).

Atomic force microscopy, a tool for imaging, manipulating and measuring on an atomic scale.

Band gap of a semiconductor is the energy needed to free an electron from its tightly bound state in an atom to one that allows it to move freely through the crystal, conducting electricity. When the band gap is sufficiently small, the required energy can be supplied by external infrared radiation (heat) and the material can, therefore, become an infrared detector as in the 'narrow gap' semiconductors, CMT and indium antimonide.

Cast-recrystallisation-anneal, a process for producing bulk crystalline material by casting a melt of the required composition into a mould. This is then held at high temperature to induce the growth of large crystalline grains. Finally, the chemical composition of the whole is homogenised by annealing at a somewhat lower temperature.

Cathodoluminescence, a means of imaging luminescent materials in a Scanning Electron Microscope (q.v.) by bombardment with high energy electrons to produce light, as in a cathode ray tube in first generation television screens.

Chalcogenide, a compound formed between an element(s) and sulphur, selenium or tellurium.

Charge coupled device (CCD), a silicon chip that converts light into packets of electrons which it then manipulates to produce a digital signal (e.g. as an image sensor in a digital camera).

Constitutional supercooling, supercooling (q.v.) of a melt ahead of a crystallising interface caused by the segregation of a component of the melt at that interface.

Convection, commonly, the motion of a fluid produced either by buoyancy (e.g. the circulation of water in a saucepan heated from below) or that produced by mechanical means (e.g. flow in the melt induced by rotating the crystal during crystal pulling)

Dielectric, a material that does not conduct electricity but can support an electric field.

Dislocations, line defects in a crystal. The simplest form is an edge dislocation formed by the termination of an atomic layer within the crystal. A screw dislocation is a lattice displacement that results in a step being formed where the dislocation intersects a crystal surface.

Dopant, a deliberately introduced foreign atom to obtain some desired property of the crystal.

Electron beam deposition, deposition onto a substrate from a vapour produced by heating a source with an electron beam in a high vacuum.

Electron microscopy, a very high magnification technique that uses a beam of electrons rather than light to form an image of an object. *See also* **Transmission Electron Microscope** and **Scanning Electron Microscope**.

Field effect transistor (FET), a versatile device that uses an electric field to control current flow. One common use is as a low noise microwave amplifier.

Floating zone refiner, for zone refining (q.v.) materials whose melts erode all known possible container materials. The rod to be zone refined is mounted vertically and the molten zone is held in place by its surface tension.

Halide, a compound formed by an element(s) with atoms of fluorine, chlorine, bromine or iodine.

Heterojunction Bipolar Transistor (HJBT), a type of high speed transistor (q.v.) based on semiconductor layers with differing compositions, usually grown as heteroepitaxial layers, e.g. Si(Ge) on Si.

Integrated circuit, a number of components (transistors, capacitors etc.) fabricated on a single semiconductor microchip to perform a specific function (e.g. storage of data in a memory chip).

Ion implantation, a method to implant charged dopant (q.v.) atoms into a material using a large electric field.

Light emitting diode (LED), a semiconductor device that produces light when an electric current is passed through it. The wavelength of the light emitted depends on the band gap (q.v.) of the semiconductor.

Magnetic Bubble Memory, a type of computer memory that uses a thin film of a magnetic material to hold small magnetised areas known as bubbles (or domains), each storing one bit of data.

Micron, one millionth of a metre.

Molecular Beam Mass Spectrometer, an instrument that analyses the constitution of the gas in molecular beam systems such as MOMBE.

Nanostructure, an object of size intermediate between the micron and molecular scales. It can be one, two or three dimensional: for example, a very thin layer, a tiny diameter cylinder or a tiny sphere.

Photocathode, emits electrons when exposed to light. It can be used to produce images in the visible and near-infrared regions of the spectrum. Military interest was centred on improved night vision using image intensifiers.

Photoluminescence, occurs when light is absorbed by a crystal and is re-emitted, usually with a longer wavelength. It can be used to identify certain types of defect in a crystal.

Plasmonics, plasmons are density waves of electrons created when light interacts with the surface of a metal in a particular way. Plasmonics is an embryonic technology seeking to exploit this effect, e.g. to provide ultra-high speed transmission of data in faster computer chips.

Precursor, (chemistry) a substance that, after a reaction, yields a desired substance.

Pyroelectric Vidicon, a special type of camera tube that images thermal scenes by scanning an electron beam across a pyroelectric infrared detector material that is sensitive to changes in temperature.

Radio-active tracer, a small amount of a radio-active isotope of an element, the position and concentration of which can be determined by detecting the emitted products of the radio-active decay.

Rare Earth elements, a group of seventeen metals with similar properties. They were initially considered to be rare because they were present only in small amounts at the sites where they were mined. However, subsequently, large numbers of such sites have been discovered.

Scanning Electron Microscope, produces an image formed by the secondary electrons scattered from the specimen surface when it is irradiated by an incident electron beam.

Scanning Optical Microscopy, an optical microscopy technique that enables resolution of features on the surface of materials on the nanoscale, i.e. much smaller than the wavelength of the incident light.

Secondary Ion Mass Spectrometry (SIMS), a technique for analysing the near-surface regions of a specimen by sputtering (q.v.) it with an ion beam of electrically charged atoms (ions) and collecting the scattered secondary ions.

Semiconductor, a material whose electrical conductivity is intermediate between that of a metal and an insulator and which increases with increasing temperature and also when doped with certain types of atom.

Spectroscopic Ellipsometry, an optical technique that analyses the properties of thin (nanoscale) layers and surfaces of materials, based on the way they interact with light.

Sputtering, ejecting atoms from a solid surface by bombarding it with energetic particles.

Substrate, a piece of crystalline material upon which an epitaxial layer is grown. It is commonly a wafer cut from a single crystal which has been etched to remove cutting damage and then polished to obtain a very flat, clean and damage-free surface.

Superconducting ceramic, a class of materials that lose all their electrical resistance below a critical temperature.

Supercooling, approximately the amount by which the temperature of a melt is below the temperature at which its solid melts.

Supersaturation, is the measure of the degree to which the solubility of a substance in a solution or a vapour from which it is being crystallised exceeds its value when in equilibrium with that solution or vapour, i.e. neither growing nor dissolving/evaporating.

Surface acoustic wave (SAW), a sound wave that propagates along the surface of a solid.

Synchrotron, a large doughnut-shaped machine that accelerates electrons to extremely high energies, resulting in a very powerful source of X-rays.

Thermal imaging camera, forms an image of a scene at infrared wavelengths and displays it as a visual image.

Transistor, a semiconductor (q.v.) device used to amplify or switch an electronic signal.

Transmission electron microscope, an instrument that uses electrons transmitted through a thinned sample to produce images at high magnifications.

Tunnel diode, a very high frequency semiconductor device operating via an effect known as 'tunnelling'.

X-ray, a form of electromagnetic radiation used in various analytical and diagnostic techniques in science and medicine.

X-ray diffraction, a technique used to determine the basic structure of crystals such as their atomic spacing, orientation and symmetry.

X-ray (diffraction) topography, a technique for high resolution mapping of crystal defects, often used in conjunction with a second, reference crystal in double crystal X-ray (diffraction) topography.

X-ray scintillator, a material that converts X-rays into visible light.

X-ray (computed) tomography, an imaging technique that produces 3D images from a large number of 2D sections, as in a medical X-ray scanner. Often abbreviated as 'CT'.

Zone refining, a process for purifying a bar of a material by repeatedly passing a molten zone along it.

INDEX OF NAMES

THE AUTHORS

Keith Barraclough, PhD, F.Inst.P is a graduate of Birmingham University where his post-doctoral research was on optical crystals. He researched the crystal growth of semiconductors at the Clarendon Laboratory, Oxford, and at Siemens AG, Munich, before joining RSRE in 1977 to lead a team on silicon crystal growth. When RSRE became part of a government agency he held several management posts including Head of the Electronic and Optical Materials Department. He became Technical Director of Sensors and Electronics in QinetiQ and Non Executive Director of two spin-out companies. On retirement in 2003, he was instrumental in the exploitation of his research team's patents in the manufacture of silicon crystals for advanced computer chips, the subject of his next book.

Don Hurle, DSc, F.Inst.P. is a graduate of Southampton University where his PhD research involved the growth of bismuth single crystals. Recruited by RRE as a Junior Research Fellow in 1959, he spent the next thirty-two years in the Electronic Materials Division, becoming an Individual Merit scientist with an international reputation for pioneering work on several fundamental aspects of crystal growth. Awards from the American Association for Crystal Growth, the International Organisation for Crystal Growth and the University of Liège recognised his achievements. After retiring in 1991 he commissioned and edited the landmark *Handbook of Crystal Growth*, was an Honorary Visiting Professor of Industrial Physics at Bristol University and consulted to the European Space Agency's micro-gravity programme.